Concepts in Chemistry
Orbitals and Chemical Bonding

Concepts in Chemistry

Titles in this series:

Orbitals and Chemical Bonding

SI edition

P. F. Lynch B.Sc. A.R.I.C.
Head of Chemistry,
Salesian College,
Liverpool.

Longman

LONGMAN GROUP LIMITED
London
Associated companies, branches and
representatives throughout the world

© P. F. Lynch 1966
SI Edition © Longman Group Ltd 1970
All rights reserved. No part of this
publication may be reproduced, stored
in a retrieval system or transmitted in
any form or by any means—electronic,
mechanical, photocopying, recording or
otherwise—without the prior permission
of the copyright owner.

First published 1966
SI edition 1970
Second impression 1973
ISBN 0 582 32144 1

Printed in Hong Kong by
Sheck Wah Tong Printing Press

Preface

This book has been written for sixth formers and undergraduates who are meeting the concept of an electronic orbital for the first time.

The inadequacies of 'circular orbit' theory have been obvious for more than thirty years, yet it still remains the only impression of electron distribution that many sixth formers acquire. The wave mechanical treatment of the electron involves too much in the way of mathematics for a rigorous presentation. But it is a means to an end, and the results it predicts give a far better clue to the nature of the chemical bond. Nonetheless, it is important to remember that the wave approach is still no more than an acceptable model that assists in the interpretation of experimental evidence.

The Bohr theory has not been replaced by newly discovered facts, but by a somewhat better model. There are still considerable limitations, but the model has been developed on quite rigorous mathematical lines by Schrödinger and others. When tested, the developments can account for different chemical phenomena, and if we bear in mind that it is a model, the wave mechanical approach can be of value.

A brief treatment risks the appearance of being dogmatic and I have attempted to show the manner in which the results are derived wherever possible. However, the length and scope of the book are very largely dictated by the limited time available to sixth formers for extra reading.

Those pursuing the topic in greater depth will find that reference to several works will always help to clarify areas of difficulty and I have included a list of appropriate titles. I acknowledge my personal debt to the authors concerned.

SI units are used throughout this edition.

P. F. LYNCH

Contents

Acknowledgements

I would like to express my appreciation of the interest and encouragement received from my colleagues while writing the book. In particular, I am indebted to Michael Chalwin, Art Master at the College, who worked so patiently over the original drawings. I have also to thank Messrs. T. B. Kelly, T. A. Walden, J. N. Atherton and Rev. Fr. M. Blackburn, S.D.B. who checked the proofs and made many helpful suggestions, and finally the publishers for their invaluable assistance from the earliest stages.

P. F. LYNCH

1 The achievements and limitations of the Bohr theory

The electron, since its discovery, has assumed a role of increasing importance in chemistry. With the evolution of more satisfactory ideas of electronic structure, has come a widening knowledge of the chemical substances and reactions familiar to us.

In this book we will consider the development of our knowledge of the electron from the efforts of Bohr to the situation as it is at the present day. We will then deal with some particular atoms and apply the newer concepts to compound formation. It is hoped that the results of this operation, though more complex than those of earlier theory, will provide a better interpretation of the chemical and physical properties of molecules.

An atom is an essential building block of all matter. Its properties result from its components and dictate the properties of any compound in which it is included. The properties of a given atom will be modified by those of an atom with which it is associated, to give a new set of properties, which will be characteristic of the compound formed.

An atom, considered simply, consists of a nucleus possessing an overall positive charge, surrounded by negatively charged electrons. The electrons are free to move independently of the nucleus—they are certainly attracted to it—but can easily come under the influence of a second atom and its nucleus.

The nucleus, for our purposes, can be considered as a fusion of varying numbers of two fundamental particles, the proton and the neutron. The proton has an electrical charge which we describe as being positive and unit in magnitude. The neutron has an almost identical mass to that of the proton, but it is uncharged. This results in any nucleus having a net positive charge, the extent of the charge depending on the number of protons present.

We will consider the nucleus in no further depth than this. Its detailed structure is beyond the scope of this book, though the part played by the nucleus remains an appreciable one in its effect on the distribution of electrons in compounds and their resultant properties.

Of the three particles we have mentioned the electron was the first to be detected and to provide the subject of detailed study, probably because it is the most accessible.

Rays emitted from the negative electrode in a discharge tube—cathode rays—had been observed as early as 1869. Crookes, in 1879, showed that the constituents of the rays possessed a finite mass and velocity, and a negative charge. He demonstrated the former by allowing a stream of the rays to work on a paddle wheel in an evacuated tube, and the latter by noting the direction of their deflection in a magnetic field. The term 'electron' was adopted towards the end of the century, but it was left to J. J. Thomson and R. A. Millikan some years later to confirm that the electron is indeed a discrete particle. They determined its mass and charge, and showed that these quantities did not alter if either the gas in the discharge tube or the electrode material was changed.

Thomson had speculated as to the arrangement of the electrons, but his theory gave way to that of Rutherford, who in 1911 proposed an atom in which most of the mass was concentrated in the nucleus and the electrons moved at varying speeds in circular or elliptical orbits, centred on the nucleus. Soon this theory met with the criticism that on the laws of classical physics the electron, being a charged particle, would gradually fall into the nucleus as it revolved.

Rutherford's theory was rescued and placed on a firmer basis by Bohr, a Dane working with Rutherford in Manchester at the time. In 1913 Bohr suggested the application of the quantum theory of Max Planck to the electron.

Planck had been studying the radiation emitted by a heated body. The body he presumed to consist of atoms which acted as vibrators of frequency ν. From his experimental results, he concluded that instead of the vibrator being able to possess any energy, it could only have sharply defined energy values. The values were said to be *quantised*. He gave the relation between the energy E and frequency of a vibrator as:

$$E = h\nu$$

where h is the Planck constant of value $6.625\ 6 \times 10^{-34}$ Js.

The main evidence which guided Bohr to his theory was the appearance of the *hydrogen spectrum*.

If an electric discharge is passed through hydrogen gas at low pressure in a discharge tube light is emitted and it is possible to investigate the light by means of a spectrometer. This is a piece of optical apparatus which can sort out a portion of the spectrum into its component wavelengths. The result appears as a series of lines, some visible to the naked eye, while others can only be detected by using a photographic plate, sensitive to the particular part of the spectrum.—Figure 1.

Their presence had been known for some time. Towards the end of the nineteenth century Balmer had measured some of their wavelengths and had managed to produce an empirical expression which related them. Later work showed that the frequencies of the lines could be related by the expression

$$\nu = R_c \left\{ \frac{1}{n_1^2} - \frac{1}{n_2^2} \right\}$$

where n_1 and n_2 are integers and R_c is the Rydberg constant. It was left to Bohr to provide their precise explanation and he succeeded in deriving the Balmer relationship and obtaining agreement between theoretical and experimental values of the Rydberg constant.

The line spectrum of hydrogen suggested to him that the atoms of which

3

it is composed could only exist in states of sharply defined energy. The effect of the discharge would be to promote the system to a state of higher energy than before. He proposed that the system, in returning to its original energy state, would emit radiation in stepwise quantities or 'quanta'. In other words, the atoms would pass from one state to another—the stationary states—between which, emission of amounts of energy would occur, thus accounting for the various spectral lines.

Bohr's genius was to relate the electronic orbits of Rutherford with the stationary atomic states of the quantum theory. He proposed that the orbits were circular, and an electron could move in one of them without emitting energy. He also imposed an important condition on them, which limited their radii to certain values, i.e. that the angular momentum of an electron

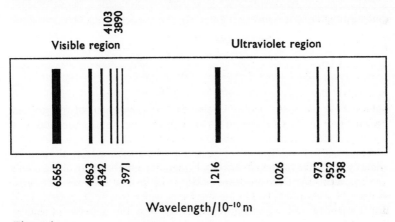

Figure 1
Part of the Hydrogen spectrum.

in one of them, could only take the value $nh/2\pi$, where n is called the Principal Quantum Number, and can take the values 1, 2, 3 etc.

The orbits were designated by the letters K, L, M etc., moving outwards from the nucleus, and Bohr decided that under normal circumstances, the electron of the hydrogen atom would take a position in the K orbit, or orbit of Principal Quantum Number $n = 1$. In this state, the most stable state, the electron will have had removed from it the greatest possible amount of energy, and if the system were to undergo a change energy would have to be *added* to it externally (in quantised units).

Let us consider the excitation of an electron from the K orbit (the *ground state* for the hydrogen electron) to the adjacent L orbit (an *excited state* for the hydrogen electron).

An electron in this state will be relatively unstable and will drop back to the ground state again. Energy will be emitted, amounting to the difference between the energies of the K and L orbits, and this will be apparent in a line of particular frequency and wavelength in the spectrum.

Quantum relation between energy and frequency is given by

$$E = h\nu$$

Frequency may be expressed by

$$\nu = \frac{c}{\lambda}$$

where c is the velocity of electromagnetic radiation, and λ is the wavelength of the radiation.

Denoting energies (stationary state energies) of the K and L orbits by E_K and E_L respectively, we have

$$E_L - E_K = \frac{h.c}{\lambda}$$

Substituting known values

$$E_K = 54.48 \times 10^{-20} \text{ J}$$
$$E_L = 217.9 \times 10^{-20} \text{ J}$$
$$h = 6.625\,6 \times 10^{-34} \text{ Js}$$
$$c = 2.997\,925 \times 10^8 \text{ m s}^{-1}$$

and solving for λ, we obtain a value for the wavelength of the emitted radiation of $1\,216 \times 10^{-10}$ m. This is a prominent line in the observed hydrogen spectrum, and we can now see how it arises.

There is also the possibility of excitation of the electron from the ground state to an orbit of higher principal quantum number than the L orbit ($n = 2$). When the electron drops back to the ground state we will again obtain an appropriate line in the spectrum, which will be characteristic of the frequency and wavelength associated with the amount of energy emitted. We may also envisage electronic excitations to orbits of high principal quantum number, followed by de-excitation, not to the ground state, but to an intermediate level.

It is obvious that the spectrum of the hydrogen atom is a good deal more involved than its quota of only one electron would suggest. However, all the lines that can be detected under low resolution can be explained on the basis of Bohr orbits, it being possible to assign a transition to all the observed frequencies.

Advances arising from Bohr's theory

Some useful consequences arose from Bohr's work in relation to the chemical properties of an element and its position in the Periodic Classification. At about the same time it had been shown that the numerical position of an element in the Periodic Table was equal to the number of protons in its nucleus, which in turn is equal to its quota of electrons, the atom being electrically neutral. Consequently periodicity in chemical properties could perhaps be related to arrangement of electrons; there had been much speculation about this, from the latter part of the nineteenth century up to that time.

Bohr's explanation was a restriction on the number of electrons which could be accommodated in an orbit. The maximum number was given by the series $(2 \times n^2)$, where n is again the principal quantum number. His restriction was given support by the apparent electronic similarities which occurred when it was applied to well-known groups of elements.

Thus the chemical likeness of the alkali metals was explained electronically by allocating electrons into the available orbits.

The element lithium, the third element in the Periodic Table, has three protons in its nucleus—we say it has an *atomic number* of three—so it will have three extranuclear electrons in each of its atoms.

Sodium has an atomic number of eleven, and its atoms will contain eleven electrons. We may apply Bohr's propositions and allocate the available electrons into orbits, bearing in mind that the electrons will try to occupy the orbit of lowest energy as far as possible.

	K $n = 1$	L $n = 2$	M $n = 3$
At.No. 3 Lithium	••	•	
At.No. 11 Sodium	••	•••• ••••	•

It can be seen that both lithium and sodium have only one electron in their outermost orbits. If we tried the same thing for potassium (atomic number 19), we would have nine electrons in the outer orbit, and we would have to envisage some sort of subdivision—this we will leave for the moment.

We may approach the noble gases in the same way—we will be content with three of them:

	K	L	M
At.No. 2 Helium	••		
At.No. 10 Neon	••	•••• ••••	
At.No. 18 Argon	••	•••• ••••	•••• ••••

In the elements helium and neon we have a completely filled outer orbit, and in argon we have eight electrons in the outer orbit.

A noble gas became the basis of a concept of bonding. It was proposed that each element, in forming compounds, would, if possible, attain the structure of the noble gas nearest to it in the Periodic Table. The stability of the known noble gases, which was unparalleled, was attributed to the fact that they either possessed a completely filled outer orbit, or one containing eight electrons.

6

In 1916 Kossel and Lewis appreciated the significance that a noble gas always appeared between an alkali metal and a halogen in the Periodic Table, and they applied the orbit concept to the theoretical formation of sodium chloride. They suggested that if a sodium atom lost its outermost electron, and was accepted by a chlorine atom, then both the elements would assume electronic structures of noble gases, with their consequent stability.

Thus:

Initial state	Na (2.8.1)
	Cl (2.8.7)
Final state	Na$^+$ (2.8)
	Cl$^-$ (2.8.8)

The structure 2.8 is that of the noble gas neon, while the structure 2.8.8 is that of argon.

The final states of the sodium and chlorine atoms would possess an electronic charge—one unit positive in the case of the sodium atom, because it now has one electron less than it has protons; and one unit negative, since it has gained an electron in the process, for the chlorine atom. These final states of the sodium and chlorine atoms are known as *ions*. The sodium atom becomes a positive ion Na$^+$, and the chlorine atom becomes a negative ion Cl$^-$. The attraction between oppositely charged species would constitute a bond and in this case the bond is said to be *ionic* or *electrovalent*. Since the sodium atom, in forming a bond lost one electron, and the chlorine atom gained one electron, both these atoms are said to have a valency of one; for sodium, it is equal to the number of electrons in its outermost orbit. For the chlorine atom, the valency can be seen to be equal to eight minus the number of electrons in its outer orbit.

A B

(Only the outer electrons are shown.)

It should be pointed out that this kind of idea, though less clearly defined, had been put forward much earlier than this, by such workers as Davy and Berzelius in the early part of the nineteenth century, and by Abegg and J. J. Thomson, in a rather more refined approach, about a hundred years later.

A second type of bond was envisaged by Lewis and later by Langmuir in 1919. We have already seen that a chlorine atom has an electronic configuration one short of the noble gas argon. We also know that chlorine forms a stable diatomic molecule Cl_2. It would be impossible to obtain an ionic bond of the type discussed earlier, between two chlorine atoms, which would give rise to a stable molecule.

Langmuir considered the chlorine atoms to take part in a *covalent* bond, where one of the outermost electrons on each chlorine atom was mutually shared to give a noble gas structure to both atoms.

This mechanism, in which there is no *transfer* of an electron from one chlorine atom to the other is depicted above.

In this illustration, the electrons belonging to atom A are represented as •, while those belonging to B are shown as ×. On sharing, both atoms attain eight electrons as an outer configuration.

Bohr's theory provided the sound foundation for the wealth of valency theory which followed. Examples have been quoted for two simple substances, as considerable extension and improvement to the original Bohr theory took place in the succeeding years.

Limitations of the Bohr theory

The sharp lines of the hydrogen spectrum had been investigated by Paschen using equipment of high resolution, who found that they did not appear as single lines, but as several lines of small separation. The magnitude of the separations would indicate a small difference in frequency between them, which in turn would indicate a small difference (in terms of energy) between certain new states. This energy difference is too small to be accounted for by any of the possible excitations from one Bohr orbit to another, since the energy differences involved in these are a lot larger.

The problem was approached by Sommerfeld in 1915. He extended Bohr's concept of circular orbits to include the possibility that the electron could move in an elliptical path.

Sommerfeld's work required the introduction of a second quantum number which was denoted by the letter k; it was known as the subsidiary quantum number. The value of k is related to the geometry of an ellipse, and the ratio n/k, where n is the principal quantum number, is equal to the ratio of the semi-major to the semi-minor axes of the ellipse.

The quantum number k could take the values 1, 2, 3, etc., and for a particular value of the principal quantum number, as k increases, the shape of the ellipse goes from a thin elongated form, to that of a circle.

Once we accept the possibility of an elliptical orbit, we must take into account a change in the velocity of an electron undertaking such an orbit relative to a circular one. Relativity theory predicts an associated change in mass for the electron, and as a result the energy of an electron describing an ellipse of say, principal quantum number $n = 3$, subsidiary quantum number $k = 1$, will be different to that of an electron in an orbit for which $n = 3$ and $k = 2$.

The magnitude of the energy difference visualised here is relatively small and the concept provides the possibility of new energy levels of small separation.

If we now reconsider the closely spaced lines that appeared in the spectrum of the hydrogen atom under higher resolution, we can see that it is possible to explain these by excitations and de-excitations between such energy levels. Such transitions would result in emissions of small amounts of energy—small enough to account for the energy differences characterised by closely spaced lines.

The notation of s, p, d, and f levels was introduced (from spectroscopic terminology) to distinguish the different values of k and their corresponding orbits. We will not discuss these at the moment, but reintroduce them in the light of later work, when they will be of more value.

The work of Sommerfeld did not provide the complete answer, for we come across more lines in the spectrum of the hydrogen atom under closer examination. These cannot be explained on the basis of a simple Bohr theory, or when the refinements of Sommerfeld are taken into account. The additional lines require the introduction of two new quantum numbers. If we imagine the electron moving in an orbit, circular or elliptical, then as the electron is charged, a magnetic field is produced in a manner similar to that produced when current flows in a coil. The electron behaves as a magnet as it spins on its own axis and there will be a field interaction. The energy change experienced by the electron will be governed by the direction of the spin, clockwise or anticlockwise, in relation to the direction of orbital travel. The two spin modes are associated with two energy levels and a third quantum number m_s—the spin quantum number, is introduced to cover these. It can take the value $+\frac{1}{2}$, $-\frac{1}{2}$. As the new levels are closely spaced, they will account for relatively minute transitions of the electron, resulting in only very small emissions of energy, and hence spectral lines which are close together.

When the hydrogen gas is placed in an external magnetic field, more lines appear in the spectrum, and these are accounted for by what is termed the 'Zeeman Effect'. Under a magnetic influence, the plane of the electron orbit can be orientated in definite directions. The possible orientations can be associated with a fourth quantum number, which characterises the new energy levels produced. It is known as the *magnetic quantum number, m*. This can take the values 0, ± 1, ± 2 etc.

The introduction of new quantum numbers considerably complicates the picture, and we must remember that the hydrogen atom we are considering contains only one electron; in other words, this is the simplest case we can have. In fact the serious objection was apparent, that the Bohr theory was incapable of predicting the spectra of systems with more than one electron. An additional failing was its inability to account for the relative intensities of the spectral lines.

In the next chapter, the electron is treated in a different manner. We retain from Bohr theory, the concept of quantum numbers. In other words, the energy of an electron, which depends on its distance from the nucleus, and to what magnetic and electric fields it is subjected, is defined by a set of parameters and it is the values which these take, that 'label' any electron. Thus, the information $n=2$; $k=2$; $m=0$; $m_s.=\frac{1}{2}$ characterises a unique electron in an atom and tells us its energy and position, or more correctly as we shall discover, its probable whereabouts.

2 The electron considered as a wave motion

It is customary for physicists to view light either as a movement of small particles or as a wave motion. For the phenomena of diffraction and interference, only when light is considered as a wave motion, does the theory satisfactorily explain observable effects.

In 1924, de Broglie suggested that the electron might be considered as a wave motion, and he proposed a relationship; now the de Broglie equation for an electron:

$$\lambda = \frac{h}{p}$$

where p is its momentum, λ its wavelength and h is the Planck constant.

The problem now was to see if this could be supported. If the electron was a wave, then it should be able to produce diffraction or interference phenomena. Diffraction, the formation of light and dark patterns by the incidence of light on a series of very small obstacles, requires a diffraction grating of suitable characteristics. The size of the 'obstacles' has to be of the same order of magnitude as the wave-length of the light.

In 1927, Davisson and Germer showed that the spacings of the atoms in a crystal could be used as diffraction gratings, since these compared with the values that de Broglie had calculated for electron wavelengths.

On bombardment of the crystal with a stream of electrons diffraction patterns are observed, consisting of light and dark rings, and they can be obtained on a photographic plate. The dark rings depict areas of high electron density while the lighter ones depict areas of low density.

If we accept a wave theory to explain such effects and wish to consider the electron as a wave, then what we want now is a relation between a property of the wave and electron density. This property is in fact the square of the amplitude of the wave, and it is obtained from a 'wave equation' which describes the electron.

Before we discover more about the wave equation, we should mention an important statement made in 1927, which is of vital significance to our study. It is known as the Heisenberg Uncertainty Principle, and it states in effect 'that it is not possible to predict at the same time both the position and the momentum of an electron'.

In other words, if we are considering an electron of some particular momentum, we are unable to state its exact position and vice versa. This principle is rooted in the nature of the electron, a very small particle having a very high velocity. Consequently we are not entitled to talk of precise positions of electrons of given momentum, but we must replace such statements by those of *probability* that an electron will be in a given position.

As an example, we can apply the Uncertainty Principle to the diffraction patterns. We can say that the dark parts on the photographic plate, which represent points of high electron density, now refer to points where we have

10

the greatest probability of finding an electron in a volume about those points.

Perhaps this idea of probability and particle density can be visualised more easily by the following analogy.

Suppose we construct a map of the British Isles and by means of dots we represent all the people who speak with a Birmingham accent throughout the country. We will find the greatest concentration of dots in the Birmingham area itself, with an appreciable concentration in the outer city area and its surrounding towns. The concentration of dots will diminish rapidly outside this. However, there will be dots at a considerable distance from Birmingham—probably as far as the North of Scotland and the West of Ireland. In other words, there is a small but finite chance of hearing the accent at a relatively large distance from the area of greatest concentration.

However, if we cut off most of the probability by enclosing the bulk of the dots by a boundary (it will probably be circular) we can say that this shape represents the greatest probability of hearing the accent in the British Isles. Thus we have represented the probability by a geometric shape.

It is as well not to take the analogy too seriously. However, a very similar picture holds for the electron in an atom. We will see later that we may construct a shape to represent the greatest probability of finding a particular electron, but that there is a finite chance that it may be found outside this. We are unable to say exactly that we will hear the accent at a particular place, but that we are most likely to hear it in an area, with the chance that it may be heard really anywhere, both the accent and the electron being constantly in motion.

We have already mentioned the existence of a wave equation; this was devised by Schrödinger in 1926, who composed an equation to describe the wave motion of an electron. We will state the equation in the form it usually takes, but first to get some idea of the way in which such a thing can be arrived at, we may demonstrate the origin of the equation by the following, which is by no means a proof.

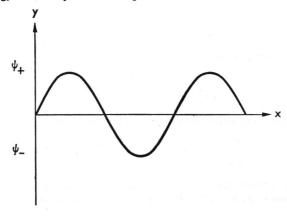

Consider a wave of amplitude ψ progressing along the x axis. The wave will have positive and negative amplitudes. We will represent the probability of the position of the electron by ψ^2 to accommodate this, where ψ will be the wave function for the electron.

The probability of finding the electron in a volume dv will be $\psi^2 dv$. The electron must be found somewhere, i.e. integrating over the whole of space:

$$\int \psi^2 \, dv = 1$$

Now $\psi = f(x), f'(t), f''(\lambda)$, where t is the time and λ is the wavelength. We want an equation which will vary ψ with distance x; in other words we want to find how the probability alters with distance (say from the nucleus). A suitable one is:

$$\psi = A \sin 2\pi \left(\frac{x}{\lambda} - vt\right) \qquad \text{where } v \text{ is the frequency.}$$

In the form of a differential equation, eliminating v and t,

this becomes:
$$\frac{d^2\psi}{dx^2} + \left(\frac{2\pi}{\lambda}\right)^2 \psi = 0 \qquad (1)$$

We have already met the equation (on page 9):

$$\lambda = \frac{h}{p} = \frac{h}{mv} \qquad (2)$$

where v is the velocity and p is the momentum of the particle. The kinetic energy of the electron is given by:

$$E_K = \tfrac{1}{2}mv^2 \qquad (3)$$

Combining equations (2) and (3), we get:

$$\lambda = \frac{h}{m.\sqrt{\dfrac{2E_K}{m}}}$$

Substituting in equation (1), we get:

$$\frac{d^2\psi}{dx^2} + \frac{4\pi^2.m^2.2E_K}{mh^2}.\psi = 0$$

Simplifying and expanding for the x, y, and z axes, we get:

$$\frac{d^2\psi}{dx^2} + \frac{d^2\psi}{dy^2} + \frac{d^2\psi}{dz^2} + \frac{8\pi^2 m.E_K}{h^2}.\psi = 0$$

We may improve this by taking into account the change in mass of the electron from relativity, and replacing m by μ *the reduced mass.*

The Schrödinger wave equation

$$\nabla^2 \psi + \frac{8\pi^2 m}{h^2}.(E-V)\psi = 0$$

where

$$\nabla^2 \psi = \frac{\partial^2 \psi}{dx^2} + \frac{\partial^2 \psi}{dy^2} + \frac{\partial^2 \psi}{dz^2}$$

ψ is the wave function for the electron; m is the mass of the electron; E is the total energy of the electron; V is the potential energy of the electron; and x, y, z are normal coordinates.

The symbol ψ in the wave equation for an electron is a function of the amplitude of the wave, and the probability of finding the electron is related to the square of the wave amplitude. We have also seen the probability in terms of particle density.

And so we have a tangible relationship between a practical quantity—the electron density in a particular volume, and ψ, the wave function in the wave equation, where it is related to position on x, y and z axes.

The wave equation can provide us with a new picture of the state of the electron in the hydrogen atom. If known values for the energy levels of the hydrogen electron are substituted, satisfactory solutions for ψ can be obtained. The important, and convincing fact, is, that only when E takes the exact values for the energy levels, can acceptable solutions for ψ be obtained. In other words, there are really an infinite number of possible solutions from the wave equation, but by imposing conditions on the equation to make it fit in with observed phenomena we can obtain a sensible solution which describes the hydrogen electron; that is, a theoretical expression, with real physical significance.

After a transformation of the equation into polar coordinates, it is necessary to introduce several terms, and we again find that because of what we know about the electron, we have to place a limit on the values which the terms can take. The terms, as in Chapter 1, label the electron.

After selection, for each solution of ψ, there is only one acceptable value of E, and everything else about the electron is contained in ψ.

The terms, with their selective values, are the quantum numbers of the wave theory, and they arise as a combination of mathematical necessity and physical observation.

We have the *principal quantum number n*, where n can take the values 1, 2, 3, etc.

The second quantum number required by the wave theory replaces the subsidiary quantum number of the older theory. It is known as the *azimuthal quantum number*, and it is denoted by the letter l. It can take the values 0, 1, 2, etc., and they equal the old k values minus one in each case.

The existence of a *magnetic quantum number* is also required by the wave equation, but again, it arises as a fundamental necessity. It is denoted by the letter m, and it can take the values 0, ± 1, ± 2 etc.

We may use the wave equation in consideration of the hydrogen electron in its ground state—i.e. when the principal quantum number $n = 1$. Under this condition, we can obtain a satisfactory solution for ψ, only when the condition that when $l = 0$, $m = 0$ applies; and ψ provides us with an expression which will give us information as to the whereabouts of the hydrogen electron.

The square of this function, as was mentioned previously, represents the probability of finding an electron in some given volume, or the particle density in the volume.

The expression does not however, provide us with a statement of the exact path of the hydrogen electron,† and so we will not call it an expression for the orbit of principal quantum number $n = 1$.

We introduce a new term to avoid any possible confusion arising from the older theory. The expression for the wave function ψ when the condition $m = 0$, $l = 0$, $n = 1$ is satisfied, is called the expression for the *1s orbital*.

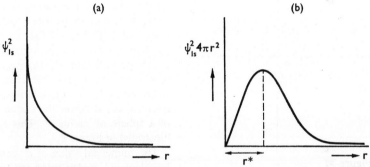

Figures 2a and b

(a) Graph to show dependence of ψ^2_{1s} with r. (b) Graph to show dependence of $\psi^2_{1s} 4\pi r^2$.

The figure 1 indicates that it is an orbital of principal quantum number $n = 1$, and the condition that when $l = 0$, $m = 0$ is expressed in the use of the letter s. The nomenclature was introduced by spectroscopists in earlier work, with reference to the quantum numbers on the elliptical orbit theory. Its use is retained now, but its significance is altered.

The square of this function, we have already learned, is related to probability and particle density. In this case the function turns out to be spherically symmetrical; in other words, the probability of finding the electron, or the particle density, is the same in all directions in space.

If a graph is plotted of ψ^2_{1s} against r, where r is the distance from the nucleus, we obtain a graph which is shown as Figure 2a. From the graph, we can see that the probability of finding the electron in a volume element

† Originally, Schrödinger thought of his waveforms as representing the *actual* distribution of the electron. Born introduced the idea of probability in 1926, which led to Heisenberg's Uncertainty Principle of 1927.

close to the nucleus is high and that this probability falls steeply as the distance from the nucleus increases. There is also a very small but finite chance of finding the electron at a relatively very large distance from the nucleus (we have already met this possibility in our earlier analogy), and this chance is still finite at relatively huge distances from the nucleus.

The expression ψ_{1s}^2, however, is not the most useful property we can obtain, for although the probability of finding the electron very close to the nucleus is greatest, there is only a small volume element there, and so the actual distribution would look rather different.

If we plot ψ_{1s}^2 times the volume element $(4\pi r^2)$ enclosed at a particular radius, then the result appears as the combination of Figure 2a and a plot of volume element against r. The result of this is shown in Figure 2b.

The product $\psi_{1s}^2 . 4\pi r^2$ is known as the 'radial probability distribution'. We can interpret it thus: The actual probability rises with the magnitude of r, and reaches a maximum when r has a value which we will call r^*. In other words, the most probable place where we could find the hydrogen electron would be on the surface of a sphere of radius r^*. This is illustrated in Figure 3.

The numerical value of r^* can be calculated, and it turns out to be 0.529×10^{-10} m. This is precisely the same value as that for the radius of the K orbit on the older Bohr theory.

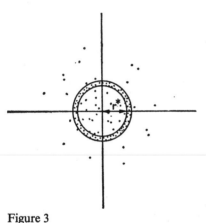

Figure 3

Illustration of the most probable place where the electron might be found—i.e. on the surface of hypothetical sphere of radius r^*.

But this is the distinction between the result obtained from using wave theory to that obtained from the older theory.

We now describe the position of the hydrogen electron by an orbital which we call the 1s orbital. By this we mean that the electron could be anywhere relative to the nucleus as centre, but that there is a maximum probability of finding the electron on a spherical surface of radius 0.529×10^{-10} m, with the nucleus as centre (the value of the radius of the Bohr K orbit). But whereas the Bohr theory confines the electron to a fixed orbit of this radius, the orbital allows an appreciable chance of the electron being either closer to the nucleus than this, or further away.

The problem now is how to represent the hydrogen 1s electron diagrammatically. We know where it is most probably to be found, and we could draw a thin spherical shell of some radius to represent this. However, we have already met, in our previous analogy, the possibility of drawing a boundary surface which encloses nearly all of the probability of finding the electron. In the case of the 1s electron, the boundary will be spherical, and it is normally represented by a circle. It should be pointed out that this boundary surface is not the actual orbital. The orbital is the function ψ— we have been plotting functions of ψ^2 and the sphere enclosing most of the probability will have the same shape, i.e. the same dependence on r, as ψ^2. Figure 4 shows the boundary.

However, the shape of the function ψ is the same as that for the function ψ^2 in the case of s orbitals, and we may summarise as follows. The hydrogen electron in the 1s level can be expressed by an orbital which is spherical in shape, the orbital being a volume in which we have very nearly all the probability of finding the electron.

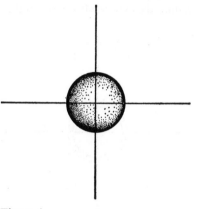

Having considered an electron in the hydrogen atom of principal quantum number $n=1$, we may now investigate the results provided by the wave equation for higher principal quantum numbers than this. Again, it is found that satisfactory solutions can only be obtained if we accept the existence of quantum numbers; they, however, arise quite fundamentally.

For an electron of principal quantum number $n=2$, we can again apply the wave equation,

Figure 4

Representation of 1s orbital—a boundary surface to enclose most of the probability of finding a 1s electron

and for satisfactory solutions, the condition imposed is that l can have two possible values with particular values of m:

$$\text{i.e. when } l = 0, m = 0$$
$$l = 1, m = 0, \pm 1$$

These are the only sets of conditions which provide acceptable solutions to the wave equation for principal quantum number $n=2$. We will deal with the two sets of conditions separately.

When $n=2$, $l=0$, $m=0$

We may again obtain an expression for the function ψ and calculate values for the function $\psi^2 . 4\pi r^2$ with variation in r, and construct a 'radial probability curve'. The result is shown in Figure 5.

From the graph, it can be seen that there are two maxima, i.e. there will be two spherical surfaces on which the electron is most likely to be found.

16

The electron distribution is spherically symmetrical and we may again represent the state of an electron in this energy level by an *s* orbital, i.e. we may draw a circle (sphere) to enclose nearly all the probability of finding the electron in this particular level. Because it is an orbital of principal quantum number $n = 2$, we call the orbital a $2s$ orbital.

We have mentioned that in this case there will be two surfaces of 'maximum probability'; the other distinction is that the overall probability extends further into space, and this will result in the boundary surface being of larger radius than that for the $1s$ orbital. We need not worry about the distinction between the function ψ and $\psi^2 . 4\pi r^2$, but the point should be kept in mind.

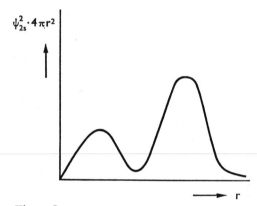

$\psi_{2s}^2 \cdot 4\pi r^2$

r

Figure 5

Graph to show dependence of $\psi^2 . 4\pi r^2$ with r for a $2s$ electron.

When $n = 2$, $l = 1$, $m = 0$, ± 1

Solution of the wave equation for these conditions, would give three expressions for the wave function ψ, and we could again plot 'radial probability distributions'. These are not shown, but in all cases, the probability is zero at the origin, rises to a maximum value and decreases as r becomes large. We may again construct surfaces which will enclose nearly all the probability of finding an electron with the above values of the quantum numbers.

They are shown in Figure 6. The three are of the same shape but extend in different directions in space. The corresponding orbitals are called the $2p_x$, $2p_y$ and $2p_z$ orbitals respectively. The letter p is retained from the earlier nomenclature of the spectroscopists, and is characteristic of this value of l.

The wave functions $\psi_{2p_x, 2p_y, 2p_z}$ are not spherically symmetrical, i.e. the probability does not extend equally in all directions in space and as can be seen from the diagrams, the maximum extension is in a different plane in each case; i.e. along the x, y and z axes respectively.

A further point is that the shapes of the orbitals, i.e. the functions ψ, are not quite the same as the surfaces, i.e. the functions $\psi^2 . 4\pi r^2$. The shape of the orbitals is in fact two spheres touching at the origin. However, it is the probability of where the electron is that concerns us, and we invariably use the shapes as shown in Figure 6 when talking about a $2p$ electron.

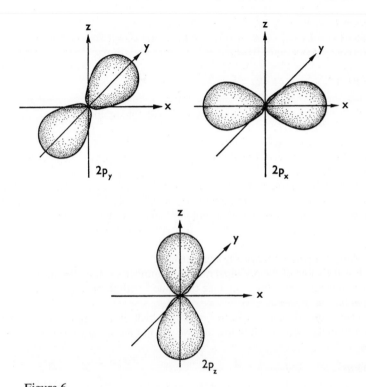

Figure 6

Surfaces to show the dependence of $\psi^2 . 4\pi r^2$ with r for electrons for which $n=2$, $l=1$, $m=0$, ± 1. They are used as representations of $2p$ orbitals.

For principal quantum number $n=2$, therefore, we have the possibility of the electron occupying two different states, the $2s$ and the $2p$ orbitals.

We will now consider the case for principal quantum number $n=3$. Solution of the wave equation affords satisfactory solutions for the following conditions:

$$\text{When } l = 0; m = 0 \quad (s\text{-type})$$
$$l = 1; m = 0, \pm 1 \quad (p\text{-types})$$
$$l = 2; m = 0, \pm 1, \pm 2 \quad (d\text{-types})$$

When $n=3$, $l=0$; $m=0$

The function ψ is spherically symmetrical and we have an s orbital. It is similar to the $1s$ and $2s$, but this has three surfaces of high probability and the overall probability sphere will extend further into space. It is called the $3s$ orbital.

When $n=3$, $l=1$; $m=0$, ± 1

The three functions ψ are not spherically symmetrical—we obtain p orbitals and they are called the $3p_x$, $3p_y$ and $3p_z$ orbitals.

When $n=3$, $l=2$; $m=0$, ± 1, ± 2

When the value for the azimuthal quantum number l is 2, the wave equation will give five satisfactory solutions, with five corresponding m values. We may construct surfaces to enclose most of the probability as before. They are shown in Figure 7. The five functions ψ are known as the $3d$ orbitals, the letter d, retained from spectroscopic terminology, being characteristic of the value of l.

Four of the boundary surfaces (those for $m=\pm 1$, ± 2) are similar in shape but extend in different directions in space. The surface for the $\psi_{3d}^2 . 4\pi r^2$ function when $m=0$ is rather different. The electron concentration is mostly along the z axis, but there is a circular shell about the origin in the xy plane.

None of them is spherically symmetrical.

For the value of the principal quantum number $n=4$, we obtain s, p and d orbitals again but now l can take the value 3 with seven associated values of m ($m=0$, ± 1, ± 2, ± 3).

These conditions give rise to f orbitals which bear a similarity in shape to d orbitals; they are complex, and we will not discuss them further.

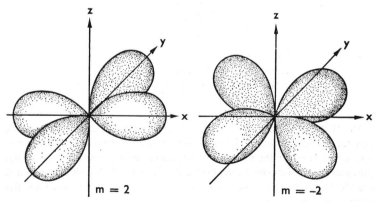

Figure 7a

Surfaces drawn to enclose most of the probability of finding an electron for which $n=3$, $l=2$, $m=\pm 2$.

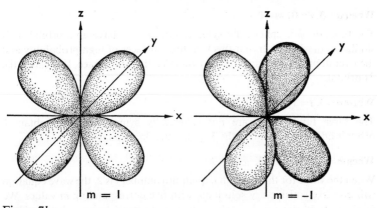

Figure 7*b*
Surfaces drawn to enclose most of the probability of finding an electron, for which $n=3, l=2, m=\pm 1$.

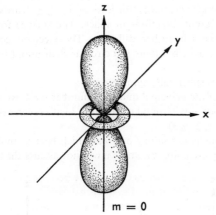

Figure 7*c*
Surface drawn to enclose most of the probability of finding an electron for which $n=3, l=2, m=0$.

One of the satisfying results from this treatment of the electron using wave mechanics is that an elaborate application of the wave equation can explain satisfactorily the numerous lines that appear in the spectrum of the hydrogen atom, discussed in the first part of this book. In other words, it is possible to predict that there will be differences in energy between the different orbitals of a particular principal quantum number.

The main virtue of the approach is the far more satisfying picture we obtain when we study the role played by the electron in the bonding between atoms to form a molecule.

3 The electronic configurations of the elements

The Pauli exclusion principle

Before we discuss the use of orbitals in bonding, there is an important principle that we should state at this point.

It was stated by Pauli in 1925 and is known as the *Pauli exclusion principle*: 'In any system, whether a single atom, or a molecule, no two electrons can be assigned the same set of four quantum numbers.'

The principle may be expressed physically: if two electrons have identical parameters, then they will be in the same place at the same time; but there is no mathematical proof of the principle.

In the first chapter, we mentioned the existence of the spin quantum number in the earlier theory, in order to explain some of the lines which were observed in the hydrogen spectrum under high resolution.

Now, the existence of such a quantum number is not required for satisfactory solutions of the Schrödinger wave equation in any of the cases we have discussed. However, investigation of the spectrum of helium suggests that its two electrons go into the $1s$ orbital with opposite spins.

Investigation of the next element, lithium, with three electrons, suggests that two of the electrons go into the $1s$ level, and the next, instead of trying to occupy the level of lowest energy (the $1s$), takes a position in the $2s$ orbital.

It seems, therefore, that as there are only two possible spin values for an electron (assuming the existence of the spin quantum number), and both these values have already been assumed by the two electrons in the $1s$ orbital, the third electron decides to occupy an orbital of a different set of quantum numbers (i.e. either n, m, or l different). In other words, if the third electron did enter the $1s$ orbital, its four quantum numbers would have precisely the same values as one of the electrons already in the orbital. Since this is not found to occur, i.e. the third electron enters the $2s$ orbital, it seems that all electrons take up positions so that at least one of their quantum numbers is different to that of any electron already in the atom. Any orbital then, can only accommodate a maximum of two electrons.

We have said that the fourth (spin) quantum number is not required by Schrödinger's wave equation. However, in 1928 Dirac derived a system of quantum mechanics, involving relativity, and he actually obtained terms which corresponded to this quantum number. His theory was also responsible for the prediction of the positron (a particle of equal mass to the electron but of positive charge). Unfortunately, his theory is so mathematically complex, that it has been of much less value than that of Schrödinger.

The 'aufbau' principle

In general, for relatively low atomic numbers, the energy of an orbital increases with the principal quantum number. For a particular value of the principal quantum number, the energy of an orbital increases with the notation series: s, p, d, f, though, as we will see later, the differences between these states are small for higher values of the principal quantum number, and considerable exception to the rule arises.

We have dealt with the structure of the hydrogen atom—it has one electron in the $1s$ orbital. Helium completes the building up of the $1s$ orbital with a structure $1s^2$—we commonly use this notation for convenience. The figure 1 indicates the value of the principal quantum number. The letter (s) indicates the type of orbital, and the index (2) indicates the degree of occupation, i.e. there are two electrons in this orbital.

For the element of atomic number three, lithium, the first two electrons again fill the $1s$ orbital, and the next electron, in accordance with the operation of the exclusion principle, occupies the next orbital of higher energy. The structure of lithium is therefore $1s^2 2s^1$, there being no p orbitals for principal quantum number $n = 1$.

Beryllium has a structure $1s^2 2s^2$ with a fully occupied s orbital as its outer structure.

Now we also have p orbitals for principal quantum number $n = 2$. There are three of them, the $2p_x$, $2p_y$, $2p_z$ orbitals, in the notation introduced in the last chapter.

There are some points to bear in mind in the filling up of the p orbitals It appears that electrons try to occupy orbitals in such a way that their spins are *equal* (or parallel), as far as possible. Now, the exclusion principle must operate of necessity, and so the p orbitals will normally be filled so that the electrons occupy separate orbitals as long as they can. Thus:

$2p_x^1 2p_y^1 2p_z^1$ *before* $2p_x^2 2p_y^1$
Spins parallel

These two electrons must have *opposite* spin (exclusion principle)

For the sake of brevity, we will often write the structure of say, nitrogen as $1s^2 2s^2 2p^3$, so ignoring the different states of the p orbitals that are possible, but we must remember that an orbital can only hold two electrons, and the actual structure is $1s^2 2s^2 2p_x^1 2p_y^1 2p_z^1$.

We may continue to build up in this manner from boron (At. No. 5) to neon. The building up process is often referred to as the 'aufbau' principle, whereby the structure of a particular atom is the same as the one before it in the Periodic Table plus one additional electron.

The filling of the orbitals of principal quantum number $n = 2$ (we may still call this the L shell) is marked by the element neon, with a structure $1s^2 2s^2 2p^6$. We may note in passing that this element has a completely filled outer set of p orbitals. This is often referred to as a completely filled p shell.

For the M shell, or shell of principal quantum number $n = 3$, we have the possibility of s, p, and d type orbitals. Sodium, of atomic number eleven, has the structure of neon and then one electron in the $3s$ orbital. The

Figure 8
Periodic Classification of the Elements

IA	IIA	Transition	IIIA	IVA	VA	VIA	VIIA	0
1 H $1s^1$								2 He $1s^2$
3 Li (He) $2s^1$	4 Be $2s^2$		5 B (He) $2s^2 2p^1$	6 C $2s^2 2p^2$	7 N $2s^2 2p^3$	8 O $2s^2 2p^4$	9 F $2s^2 2p^5$	10 Ne $2s^2 2p^6$
11 Na (Ne) $3s^1$	12 Mg $3s^2$		13 Al (Ne) $3s^2 3p^1$	14 Si $3s^2 3p^2$	15 P $3s^2 3p^3$	16 S $3s^2 3p^4$	17 Cl $3s^2 3p^5$	18 Ar $3s^2 3p^6$
19 K (Ar) $4s^1$	20 Ca $4s^2$	21–30	31 Ga $4s^2 4p^1$	32 Ge $4s^2 4p^2$	33 As $4s^2 4p^3$	34 Se $4p^4$	35 Br $4p^5$	36 Kr $4p^6$
37 Rb (Kr) $5s^1$	38 Sr $5s^2$	39–48	49 In $5s^2 5p^1$	50 Sn $5s^2 5p^2$	51 Sb $5p^3$	52 Te $5p^4$	53 I $5p^5$	54 Xe $5p^6$
55 Cs (Xe) $6s^1$	56 Ba $6s^2$	72–80	81 Tl $6p^1$	82 Pb $6p^2$	83 Bi $6p^3$	84 Po $6p^4$	85 At $6p^5$	86 Rn $6p^6$
87 Fr (Rn) $7s^1$	88 Ra $7s^2$	89–						

Three Series of Transition Elements (21–30, 39–48, 72–80)

21 Sc $3d^1 4s^2$	22 Ti $3d^2 4s^2$	23 V $3d^3 4s^2$	24 Cr $3d^5 4s^1$	25 Mn $3d^5 4s^2$	26 Fe $3d^6 4s^2$	27 Co $3d^7 4s^2$	28 Ni $3d^8 4s^2$	29 Cu $3d^{10} 4s^1$	30 Zn $3d^{10} 4s^2$
39 Y $4d^1 5s^2$	40 Zr $4d^2 5s^2$	41 Nb $4d^4 5s^1$	42 Mo $4d^5 5s^1$	43 Tc $4d^5 5s^2$	44 Ru $4d^7 5s^1$	45 Rh $4d^8 5s^1$	46 Pd $4d^{10}$	47 Ag $4d^{10} 5s^1$	48 Cd $4d^{10} 5s^2$
57/71 $4f^{0 \to 14}$ $5s^2$ / 72 Hf $5s^2 5p^6$ $5d^2 6s^2$	73 Ta $5d^3$	74 W $5d^4$	75 Re $5d^5$	76 Os $5d^6$	77 Ir $5d^7$	78 Pt $5d^8$	79 Au $5d^9$	80 Hg $5d^{10}$	

Elements 57–71: Lanthanide Series
Elements 89–103: Actinide Series

building up continues to include the *p* orbitals of this shell until argon, which has a structure (Neon) $3s^2 3p^6$.

Up to now, nothing has been out of place; the orbitals have been filled up in the order we would expect from the series *s*, *p*, *d*. But potassium presents the first anomaly. It would appear from spectra, that for this

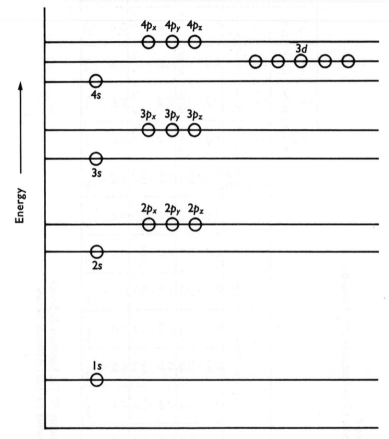

Figure 9

Orbital energy levels for a multi-electron atom. The orbitals are all represented as ○ and can accommodate a maximum of two electrons.

element, the energy of the next orbital, the 3*d*, is of higher energy than the one after that, the 4*s*. Thus the electronic structure of potassium is (Neon) $3s^2 3p^6 4s^1$ and not (Neon) $3s^2 3p^6 3d^1$. The same thing applies to the element calcium with a structure of (Neon) $3s^2 3p^6 4s^2$.

For the next element, scandium, we start to fill the 3*d* orbitals, which we had expected to have been filled first. But it appears that the energy of the

$3d$ orbitals is very little different from that of the $4s$ and electron transitions occur frequently. The element scandium is the first of the transition elements, all of which have, or can form ions which have, an incomplete inner d orbital.

The series of ten elements from scandium to zinc is known as the First Transition Series. Most of these show distinctive properties such as variable valency, coloured compounds, and complex ion formation.

There are also a second and third series of transition elements, and some of the elements in these will be mentioned later. The Periodic classification is shown in Figure 8, with the electronic configurations of the elements, and the orbital energy levels for a many-electron atom are shown in Figure 9. It is a useful exercise to write out the orbital configurations of the first dozen elements of the Periodic Table, noting the environment of the outer electrons.

4 The covalent bond

In chapter 1, we discussed rather briefly in terms of Bohr orbits, two types of chemical bond—ionic and covalent. We saw that the essential picture was that of electron transfer in an ionic bond, and a sharing of electrons in a covalent bond.

The picture remains as a foundation for the discussion of bonding in terms of orbitals. There is much evidence in support of it. The idea of ionisation had been proposed in the 1880s and the difference between electrolytes, such as sodium chloride, and non-electrolytes, such as carbon tetrachloride, had been observed quite some time before the theories of Kossel and Lewis.

Our main concern will be molecules consisting of atoms, held together by covalent bonds. It seems likely that a sharing of electrons is involved in this class of molecules. There are marked differences in molecular properties resulting from say, a Cl—Cl bond and those of sodium chloride. Whereas sodium chloride exists as an ordered array of adjacent positive and negative ions, covalent chlorine is known not to contain ions. In the former there has been electron transfer to produce oppositely charged species; in the latter there has not.

Now that we have an idea of the physical shape of the volume in which a particular electron might be found, our first problem will be to consider how effective the different shapes will be, when it comes to sharing electrons.

Consider the formation of a simple molecule AB from the atoms A and B. We may plot a potential energy curve of energy against the distance of separation of the two atoms A and B. A typical curve is shown below.

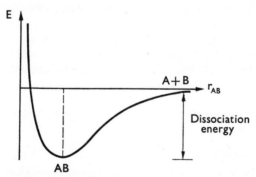

Figure 10.
Variations of energy with internuclear separation of A and B.

The energy difference between the separate atoms and the molecule is called the *dissociation energy* of the molecule. The larger the value of the dissociation energy, the more stable the molecule. It can also be seen that the most stable state for the molecule AB is at a particular separation of the atoms A and B. If we tried to push the atoms any closer together than this, the nuclei would begin to repel each other, and we would make the molecule very unstable, as can be seen from the steep rise in the energy curve for relatively small values of r.

Now it would seem likely that a bond will be strong if it is possible to obtain a good degree of overlap between two orbitals. Then both nuclei can come close to the shared electrons. On the contrary, the bond will be weak if only a small overlap is possible.

There is a mathematical basis for this. If we again consider the combination of the two atoms A and B, where A and B contain only one electron, then we may combine the wave functions for the two electrons when the atoms combine.

Writing the wave functions as ψ_A and ψ_B, the resultant probability distribution ψ^2 is given by:

$$\psi^2 = c^2(\psi_A \pm \psi_B)^2 \qquad c \text{ is a constant.}$$

This gives us an expression for the final electron density between the two nuclei, and when we consider the positive alternative solution, an extra term $2\psi_A\psi_B$ arises over and above the squares of the separate wave functions. Thus we obtain an 'extra probability' or increase in electron density between the two nuclei. This increase in the concentration of electronic charge between the nuclei lessens the natural repulsion between them. The net attractive forces between electrons and nuclei are at a maximum at the value of r corresponding to the minimum on the graph, and we can say that at this point they are sufficient to account for the formation of a stable molecule AB.

However, it will be noticed that by taking the negative alternative, we obtain 'less probability' with a reduction in electron density between the two nuclei. This could result in the formation of what is termed an anti-bond, with the resultant repulsion of the atoms concerned (see page 28). The basis of bonding in terms of orbitals is one of overlap between *singly* occupied orbitals. One can visualise it as a merger of two such electron 'clouds' as in Figure 4, page 15. In the overlap region, the increased electron density is able to pull the two positive atomic nuclei together to form a molecule.

Valence bond approach

We will now have a look at two possible ways of viewing a covalent bond between atoms. They are known as the *valence bond* method and the *molecular orbital* method. We will consider the theory of the methods separately and judge the merits of both approaches when we come to examples later.

In chapter 1 we mentioned early theories of bonding, and when we considered the formation of a molecule of chlorine from two chlorine atoms, we drew structures for both chlorine atoms to show the outer electronic configurations. We then considered the covalent bond to result from a sharing of two electrons, one from each atom. This is, in essence, the valence bond approach to covalent bonding. With our knowledge of orbitals, we would now consider the bond to be formed by overlap of the partly filled atomic orbitals of each atom—the outer orbitals, in each case. Writing out the electronic structure of chlorine as $1s^2\,2s^2\,2p^6\,3s^2\,3p_x^2\,3p_y^2\,3p_z^1$ we can see that the p_z orbital of each atom will be responsible for the bond. Here the success of the sharing will be reflected in the strength of the bond and it will depend on the degree of overlap. However, there are several extensions to this theory, and we will introduce them when they become necessary in the structures of certain molecules.

We should at this point introduce an important concept which has significance in valence bond theory; it is that of *resonance*. We will meet cases of molecules later on, when it seems impossible to construct a satisfactory picture for the bonding. Such a case is the benzene molecule. We may write down the Kekulé structure for benzene, and then a similar structure with the double bonds alternated. There are also other possible structures for benzene due to Dewar. We may write each of the structures by an approximate wave function and combine the wave functions to give a new resultant wave function. The contributions of some of the individual functions will be 'weighted' more favourably than others if they will be more important in the final structure. The expression for the new wave function is of lower energy than that of any of the original ones. In other words, the 'blended' wave function gives the more stable state and it seems reasonable that this is nearer to the actual structure than any of the original conventional ones. In the case of benzene, the measured bond length between two carbon atoms is 1.39×10^{-10} m and only one value can be isolated. The standard single carbon–carbon bond length is 1.54×10^{-10} m, and that for a carbon–carbon double bond is found to be 1.32×10^{-10} m.

It would seem therefore, that the actual state is one somewhere between a carbon–carbon single bond and a double bond, though rather nearer a double bond in character. We may express this on resonance theory, by saying that the true structure of benzene is a *resonance hybrid* of several structures, where the actual structure is more stable than any of the writable conventional ones. It should be pointed out that the hybrid is not the result of an oscillation between such structures, nor does the benzene molecule contain certain percentages of the structures.

The hybrid is a completely new structure; its properties are distinctive and unique and are not those of one of the possible conventional ones. This is more successful in explaining the known chemical properties of the molecule than thinking in terms of one structure.

In valence bond theory, then, we may have to call on the idea of resonance to help us out, as we may only be able to write an approximate wave function for a molecule, in view of its complicated nature compared with a single atom. Extensive use is also required of another concept, hybridisation; we will meet this in the next chapter (page 35).

Molecular orbital approach

The *molecular orbital method* treats the problem in a different way. In this approach, the nuclei are considered to be in their molecular positions already; we then distribute the available electrons into new orbitals—the molecular orbitals. The molecular orbitals are associated with all the nuclei, and not with the separate atoms as was the case with atomic orbitals. However, the 'aufbau' principle applies, and electrons are fed into the orbital of lowest energy that is available, bearing in mind the operation of the Pauli exclusion principle. Thus a molecular orbital can contain only two electrons and these must have opposite spin.

The question now is that of derivation of the molecular orbitals. These orbitals can be calculated from a knowledge of the atomic orbitals of the individual atoms. The atomic orbitals are then considered in relation to the combined nuclei of the atoms taken together—this combination is known as the united atom.

We will consider the formation of some simple molecular orbitals from atomic orbitals.

If two singly occupied 1s orbitals are superimposed (one from each of two atoms), we may achieve (a) an increase in electron density or (b) a reduction in electron density between the nuclei. The former situation is characteristic of bond formation; the latter is associated with repulsion between the nuclei or antibonding. The bonding molecular orbital will contain two electrons of opposite spin (operation of the Pauli exclusion principle) whereas in the antibonding situation, the electron in each of the repelling clouds has equal or parallel spin. In the latter case, fusion of the 'probability clouds' does not occur. The energy of the antibonding molecular orbital is greater than that of the bonding orbital and greater than that of the individual atomic orbitals. Thus the two electrons will normally occupy the bonding molecular orbital and a bond will result.

Thus, when two combining nuclei are in their molecular positions, the electrons associated with them are collectively responsible for producing bonding or antibonding conditions. This is illustrated in Figure 11a for 1s orbitals.

Using the molecular orbital model of bonding, the combination of fully filled orbitals would be viewed as follows. With the nuclei in their molecular positions, four electrons would have to be distributed in the new molecular orbitals. Reference to the energy level sequence on page 30 would indicate that two electrons would enter the bonding molecular orbital and the other two would enter the antibonding orbital. This would mean, in effect, that the original atomic orbitals would be retained and bonding would not occur.

A new notation has to be introduced to label the molecular orbitals—we will introduce this in a pictorial presentation of molecular orbital formation in a few simple cases.

In Figures 11 and 12, are depicted some examples of molecular orbital formation from separate atomic orbitals. The illustrations are of surfaces like those of the atomic orbitals we drew in chapter 3; they are of greater physical significance than the actual orbitals themselves. Again we will stress the point that the boundary surfaces are functions of ψ^2, whereas the actual orbital is the function ψ.

Figure 11a depicts the formation of bonding and antibonding molecular orbitals from $1s$ atomic orbitals. The notation adopted is thus: The symbol σ is reserved for molecular orbitals which are symmetrical about the x

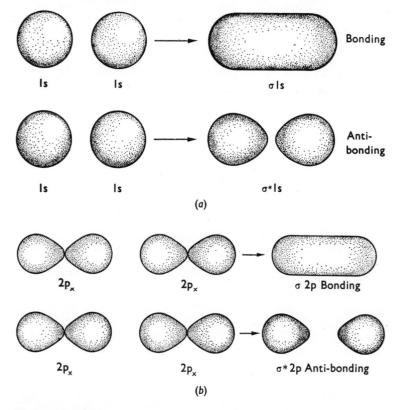

(a)

(b)

Figures 11a and b

(a) Representation of the formation of molecular orbitals from $1s$ atomic orbitals. (b) Representation of the formation of molecular orbitals from $2p_x$ atomic orbitals.

(molecular) axis. An asterisk is inserted when an antibonding orbital is the result, and the notation for the original atomic orbital is retained.

Figure 11b illustrates the formation of molecular orbitals from $2p_x$ atomic orbitals. The results are similar to those obtained from $1s$ atomic orbitals and the same notation is used.

30

Figure 12 shows molecular orbitals formed from $2p_z$ atomic orbitals. The result is the formation of $\pi 2p_z$ and $\pi^* 2p_z$ molecular orbitals. The symbol π is introduced where the resultant orbital is composed of regions of electron density about a nodal plane where the probability is zero. The nodal plane will be along the molecular axis. The molecular orbitals formed from p_y atomic orbitals are similar.

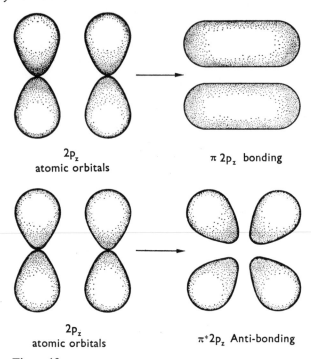

$2p_z$
atomic orbitals

$\pi\, 2p_z$ bonding

$2p_z$
atomic orbitals

$\pi^* 2p_z$ Anti-bonding

Figure 12

Representation of the formation of molecular orbitals from $2p_z$ atomic orbitals.

We will list the other molecular orbitals in the same notation in order of increasing energy as far as the $2p$, as the energies of molecular orbitals above this are uncertain.

Increase
in
energy

$\sigma 1s$
$\sigma^* 1s$
$\sigma 2s$
$\sigma^* 2s$
$\sigma 2p$
$\pi_y 2p \equiv \pi_z 2p$
$\pi_y^* 2p \equiv \pi_z^* 2p$
$\sigma^* 2p$

Thus a covalent bond may be visualised in two ways. In the valence bond treatment, we consider what happens when the two nuclei approach each other, and see what the result will be when we combine the expressions for the atomic orbitals for each atom. If the new wave function exhibits an energy minimum which is lower than the energy of the separated atoms, then it is likely that there is adequate orbital overlap. This is accompanied by an increase in electron density between the two nuclei, which provides sufficient electron–proton attraction to constitute a bond.

The molecular orbital approach considers the allocation of electrons into new orbitals associated with the whole molecule. These molecular orbitals may or may not be capable of holding the nuclei together. If the number of electrons in bonding orbitals is only equal to the number in antibonding orbitals, then there can be no resultant bond, as effectively the electrons are 'cancelled out'.

Thus a hydrogen molecule would contain two electrons, both in the $\sigma 1s$ bonding orbital, to give a strong two-electron bond. The theoretical helium molecule He_2 does not exist under normal conditions, as the four available electrons would be distributed to give two in the $\sigma 1s$ bonding orbital and two in the $\sigma^* 1s$ antibonding orbital.

On valence bond theory, the approach of two partly filled hydrogen $1s$ orbitals would result in a successful overlap of the 'probability spheres'. In the region of overlap between the two nuclei, we would have the chance of finding two electrons. This 'double' probability or increased negative charge, holds the two positive hydrogen nuclei together.

If two fully filled $1s$ orbitals of helium were to approach each other, no overlap would result, as there would be too much electronic repulsion. Looking at it another way, overlap in this case would bring the chance of finding four electrons in the orbital region between the nuclei, which would exceed the predictions of the Exclusion Principle.

5 Orbitals and the structure of molecules

Hydrogen

This atom contains just one electron in a $1s$ orbital. In bonding with a second atom, it could behave in several ways. If it lost the electron, it could become a cation H^+, i.e. a proton. However a proton is relatively very small and unstable as a single entity. In fact protons will not exist as such except in a discharge tube, but normally become attached to other molecules. An example of this is the attachment of a free proton to a water molecule in acid solution, to give the hydroxonium ion H_3O^+.

Alternatively, it could accept an electron and become an anion H^-. This does occur in the case of some hydrides, such as those of sodium and potassium, which have ionic structures similar to their chlorides.

However, most of the chemistry of hydrogen involves the formation of covalent bonds. The hydrogen molecule, on valence bond theory, may be visualised as the result of overlap of the partly filled $1s$ orbitals—one from each hydrogen atom. The overlap produces a region of increased charge, which holds the two nuclei together, successfully, as is evident in the strength of the bond in the hydrogen molecule.

On molecular orbital theory, the two electrons are fed into the molecular orbital of lowest energy—the $\sigma 1s$ bonding orbital; each electron having opposite spin. Again, the increased charge between the nuclei constitutes the covalent bond.

The hydrides of the metals will be considered along with the chemistry of the particular metal, but it is worthwhile considering the hydride of a non-metal; water at this point.

Oxygen has the electronic structure $1s^2 2s^2 2p_x^2 2p_y^1 2p_z^1$, and hydrogen has one electron in an s orbital. We will consider the structure of water on valence bond theory. Now it would seem likely that the obvious bonding mechanism in this molecule would be the overlap of the partly filled s orbitals of the hydrogen atoms with the two $2p$ orbitals ($2p_y$, $2p_z$) of the oxygen atom. This would result in two single O—H bonds. Because the p_y and p_z orbitals are at right angles to each other, we would expect the O—H bond angles to be ninety degrees. However, this theoretical picture does not fit in well with experimental observation, which would suggest a bond angle of 104° 30′. The discrepancy has been explained as being due to the mutual repulsion of the hydrogen atoms (distorting the p_y/p_z displacement), but this seems unlikely in view of their small size. The doubtful structure is shown in Figure 13. A more probable explanation comes from the concept of *hybridisation*, and we will look at the water molecule again in the light of this (page 48).

Group 1—the alkali metals

All the alkali metals have a half-filled outer s orbital, and loss of the electron from this orbital produces an ion with one positive charge, having the electronic structure of a rare gas.

The compounds of the alkali metals are almost always ionic in character, the ion being attached to a negative ion (formed by acceptance of the alkali metal electron by a non-metal), in a giant ionic crystalline lattice.

The relative ease with which the outer electron is lost, is expressed in the value of the first *ionisation energy* of the metal. This is the amount of

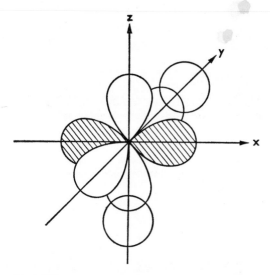

Figure 13

The water molecule viewed as the overlap of $2p_y$ and $2p_z$ orbitals of the oxygen atom with hydrogen $1s$ orbitals to produce an expected bond angle of 90°. This is not entirely satisfactory. See Fig. 21. The shaded $2p_x$ orbital constitutes the lone pair.

energy required to remove the outermost electron from a mole of gaseous atoms. Some values for the alkali metals are given below:

Ionisation energies for the outer s *electron*
(kilojoules per mole)

Li	Na	K	Rb	Cs
507	487	423	392	372

It will be noticed that the energy required decreases down the group. This is because the attraction for the outer electron by the nucleus decreases with increasing atomic size, and so rubidium will form a positive ion more readily than say, lithium.

As a result, any covalency in the chemistry of the alkali metals will occur at the top of the group, and molecules such as Na_2 and Li_2 have been detected when their metals are vaporised. Here, the bonding appears to result from the overlap of the partly filled *s* orbitals in each case.

Group 2—the alkaline earth metals

The first element beryllium, as indeed is the case with all the elements of the group, has two electrons in the outermost *s* orbital. However, beryllium

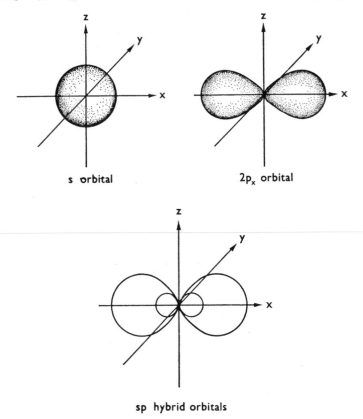

s orbital

$2p_x$ orbital

sp hybrid orbitals

Figure 14

Representation of the formation of *sp* hybrid orbitals.

is rather different from the other elements. This is a particular example of the general rule that the first element in a group tends to exhibit unique properties.

Its ionisation energy is considerably greater than that of the other Group 2 metals. The reason is, again, the small atomic radius of the beryllium atom. Coupled with this, it is much more difficult for an atom to lose an electron from a fully filled orbital—its structure being $1s^2 2s^2$—than from one which is partly filled. Thus it is difficult for beryllium to lose both its outer electrons and become a divalent positive ion. The possibility arises that the metal will form covalent bonds, where it is not required that an electron be lost. This is the case found in the chemistry of beryllium.

Two such covalent compounds of beryllium are the hydride and the chloride, with formulae BeH_2 and $BeCl_2$ respectively.

Beryllium chloride is a substance of low melting point, is non-conducting when in the molten state, and is soluble in many organic solvents. All these characteristics point to a covalent compound, but it is difficult to see how this is to result from a beryllium atom with a fully filled outer s orbital. X-ray studies have established that the molecule contains two linear Be—Cl bonds, of equal strength. The problem is solved with the introduction of a concept of hybrid orbitals.

Beryllium has a fully filled $2s$ orbital. The next available orbital, the $2p_x$ (or $2p_y$ or $2p_z$), is of pretty much the same energy, that of the $2p$ being slightly higher than that of the $2s$. It is not inconceivable that one of the $2s$ electrons gains promotion from its ground state to the $2p_x$ orbital under ordinary conditions. This would leave the beryllium atom with two half filled orbitals, $2s^1$ and $2p_x^1$. Orbitals which belong to the same atom, and that are of similar energy, are considered in a combined or *blended* state. There is a theoretical basis for this idea, and perhaps, what is more important, the theory is borne out by experimental results. Theoretically it is possible to combine the expressions for the wave functions of the $2s$ and $2p$ orbitals to give a new wave function. The orbital shape for this function is rather different from either that of the $2s$ or $2p$ orbitals because the possible electron distributions of the orbitals have combined to produce a new distribution. Two new *half filled* orbitals are formed, and they are known as *sp hybrid orbitals*, since they are formed from one s and one p orbital. They are shown in Figure 14. They extend further along the x axis than the original p orbital, and they consist of two lobes of quite different size. Since the extension along the axis is greater than for the p orbital alone, we expect and get more overlap with the chlorine p orbitals. From

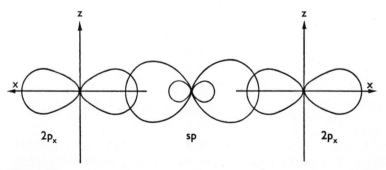

Figure 15*a*

Overlap of *sp* hybrid orbitals of beryllium with $2p_x$ orbitals of two chlorine atoms.

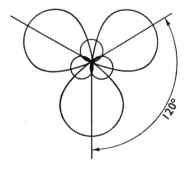

Figure 15*b*

sp^2 hybrid orbitals produced from the combination of partly filled 2*s*, 2*p_x* and 2*p_y* orbitals.

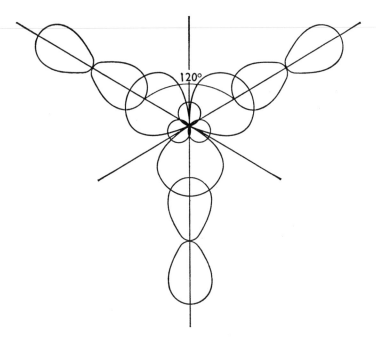

Figure 15*c*

Overlap of boron *sp*^{2} hybrid orbitals with chlorine *p* orbitals.

experimental work, we know the bonds to be linear and strong. The bonding in the $BeCl_2$ molecule is shown in Figure 15a.

Beryllium hydride is formed in a similar fashion. Here the overlap is between the sp hybrid orbitals of the beryllium atom and the partly filled $1s$ orbital from each of two hydrogen atoms, to give two covalent bonds.

The remainder of the Group 2 metals form ionic compounds almost exclusively. Their larger ionic radii, with less attraction for electrons by the nucleus, allows loss of electrons. They form divalent positive ions, since the ionisation energy for the second electron is not much greater than that for the first electron. Thus magnesium chloride has a high melting point and is conducting in the fused state; indeed, this property provides the basis for the commercial extraction of the metal.

Group 3

The Group 3 elements are characterised by a fully filled s orbital and a partly filled p orbital in their outer electron shell. It might be thought that the boron atom could lose the p electron and form a univalent positive ion B^+, but the ionisation energy for this is too high, obviously due to the proximity of this electron to the nucleus, as no such ion is found. Boron in fact, finds it impossible to form a positive ion at all. On the other hand, aluminium below it in the group, may lose both its s electrons and the p electron to form a trivalent positive ion; it also forms covalent molecules.

Boron has the structure $1s^2 2s^2 2p_x^1$, and we know that it forms a covalent compound, boron trichloride; experimental work shows that there are three equal strength B—Cl bonds in the molecule. A good explanation of this is that hybrid orbitals are formed from boron $2s$, $2p_x$ and $2p_y$ orbitals, after promotion of one of the $2s$ electrons to the $2p_y$ level. This is illustrated in Figure 15b. The hybrid orbitals lie in the same plane and are known as sp^2 hybrids, since they are formed from one s and two p orbitals. Note that each of the hybrid orbitals will be only partly filled, since there are only three electrons of principal quantum number 2 to be allocated. The layout of the BCl_3 molecule is shown in Figure 15c. The calculated bond angle for sp^2 hybrids is 120°, and this is confirmed experimentally.

Boron is a most interesting element, it being at the changeover point in the Periodic Table from metals to non-metals. It is non-metallic, and with the possibilities of hybridisation is able to form a wide range of hydrides, oxides, halides and compounds with transition elements. It is of great importance in the field of inorganic polymers.

Aluminium can form trivalent positive ions, as in the oxide Al_2O_3. The trifluoride is probably ionic also, but the anhydrous chloride is covalent. In the hydrated state, it is ionic, the Al^{+++} ion appearing to be stabilised by the presence of the water molecules.

Group 4

The leading element in the group, carbon, which will be our main concern, forms only covalent compounds. The other elements in the group—silicon, germanium, tin and lead—also tend to form covalent compounds, but an

38

increasing desire to form ionic compounds is apparent as we go down the group.

To explain a good deal of the chemistry of carbon, we need to call upon the concept of hybridisation. The electronic structure of the carbon atom is: $1s^2 2s^2 2p_x^1 2p_y^1$, or after promotion of an s electron: $1s^2 2s^1 2p_x^1 2p_y^1 2p_z^1$. All the orbitals of principal quantum number 2 are of similar energy, and

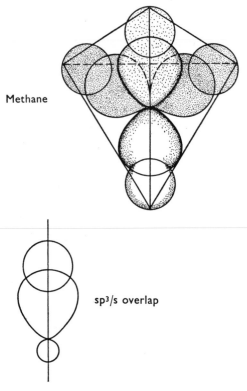

Methane

sp³/s overlap

Figure 16

Tetrahedral displacement of carbon sp^3 hybrid orbitals which overlap with hydrogen $1s$ orbitals.

we can visualise a hybridisation involving the $2s$, $2p_{x,y,z}$ orbitals. The result is the formation of four sp^3 hybrid orbitals, each one of them partly filled, since carbon has four electrons of principal quantum number 2. They are arranged tetrahedrally, at angles of 109° 31′ to each other. This explains very satisfactorily the chemistry of *methane*, where the lobes of the hybrid orbitals overlap successfully with the partly filled $1s$ orbitals from four hydrogen atoms. Figure 16 illustrates this. The tetrahedral structure accounts nicely for the equivalence of the four carbon–hydrogen bonds.

Ethane has a similar structure, each carbon being sp^3 hybridised, there being a central link between the two carbon atoms by means of one sp^3 orbital of one atom overlapping with the other. The three remaining sp^3 hybrid orbitals on each carbon atom are used to overlap with three hydrogen $1s$ orbitals. Both methane and ethane are typical saturated hydrocarbons, with the carbon exhibiting a full valency state of four. The bonds all result from end-on overlap between the orbitals, and are σ bonds.

Ethylene provides us with a second bond type. Instead of making use of sp^3 hybrid orbitals as in the methane molecule, the carbon atoms in ethylene use sp^2 hybrid orbitals, leaving a half-filled $2p$ orbital, the $2p_z$ orbital unused for the moment. The sp^2 hybrid orbitals on each carbon atom are used to overlap with (*a*) two hydrogen $1s$ orbitals and (*b*) each other. The sp^2 hybrid orbitals are arranged at 120° to one another as in the boron trichloride molecule. This is illustrated in Figure 17*a*. All the bonds in this framework are of the σ type.

The carbon atoms both have unused partly filled $2p_z$ orbitals, and it is possible for these to overlap in a *side-on* fashion. The overlap here will be appreciable, as the lobes of both extend in the same plane. However, the strength of the bond formed will not be comparable with that of the σ bonds. This new bond is a π bond. It results from overlap in two regions, above and

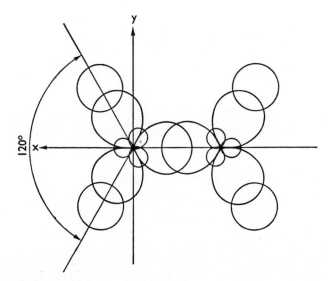

Figure 17*a*

Overlap of carbon sp^2 hybrid orbitals with hydrogen $1s$ orbitals to produce the ethylene σ bonded framework. (The axes have been changed for the sake of clarity—i.e. the z axis would be out of the plane of the paper.)

40

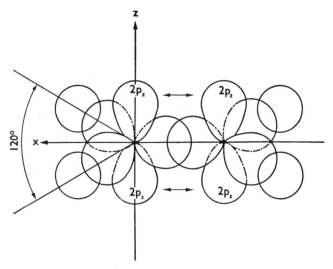

Figure 17*b*

Here the *sp*² hybrid orbitals lie in the *xy* plane. The possibility of side-on overlap of the $2p_z$ orbitals, unused in hybridisation, is also shown.

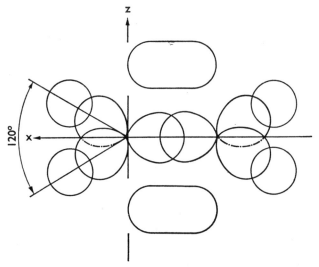

Figure 17*c*

The π molecular orbitals of ethylene in a plane perpendicular to the C—C σ bond.

below the plane of the σ bonds, the ethylene molecule possessing two bond types. Figure 17b.

The presence of the π bond accounts for the reactivity of the molecule. It is relatively weak and the electrons forming it are loosely attached; they can provide a source for electron-seeking groups, which are as a result, able to add on to the molecule. Ethylene is a typical unsaturated molecule, and this phenomenon is typical of molecules which possess a π bond.

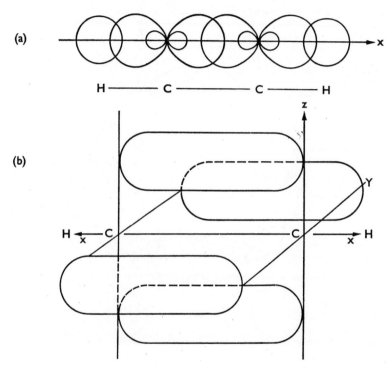

Figures 18a and b

(a) sp hybrid orbitals of carbon overlapping with themselves and hydrogen 1s orbitals. (b) The two π molecular orbitals of acetylene in mutually perpendicular planes.

On the molecular orbital theory of valency, we may consider the combination of the two unused $2p_z$ orbitals to give a π molecular orbital. The two electrons will enter the $\pi_z 2p$ bonding molecular orbital, this being of lower energy than the corresponding antibonding orbital, and consisting of two clouds above and below the σ framework.

The π bonding structure of ethylene is shown in Figure 17c.

Acetylene is well known for its addition reactions, characteristic of unsaturation, and it again contains π bonds. This time, the hybridisation is of the *sp* type and each carbon atom will have two *sp* hybrid orbitals and two unused half-filled $2p$ orbitals, the $2p_y$ and $2p_z$. The hybrid orbitals will provide bonding between (*a*) each carbon atom and (*b*) the hydrogen atoms. This basic H—C—C—H bonded framework is shown in Figure 18*a*.

Now, each carbon atom has unused partly filled $2p_y$ and $2p_z$ orbitals, and these will experience side-on overlap to give two π bonds. On molecular orbital theory, the electrons in these orbitals will enter the $\pi_y 2p$ and $\pi_z 2p$

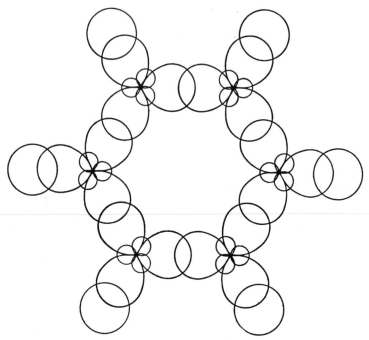

Figure 19*a*

Carbon–hydrogen framework in benzene produced by overlap of carbon sp^2 hybrid orbitals with hydrogen $1s$ orbitals. All bonds are σ bonds.

molecular orbitals, these being of lower energy than the corresponding antibonding orbitals. The two molecular orbitals are in planes at right angles to one another. Thus acetylene has two π bonds and one σ bond between the carbon atoms. The π bonding is shown in Figure 18*b*.

It will be noticed that we have been using a combination of molecular orbital theory and valence bond theory (hybridisation) to describe the last few molecules. It happens that a satisfactory picture may be obtained in this way. In other words we have considered the molecular orbital in relation to the two carbon atoms and not over the whole molecule, as would be possible on a molecular orbital theory alone. Also we have only considered the electrons which have not been needed to make up the carbon–hydrogen framework of the molecule. When the orbital, a π molecular orbital in this case, is confined to two nuclei only, we call it a *localised* molecular orbital.

The last of the compounds of carbon and hydrogen we will discuss is *benzene*. In this molecule, the carbon atoms use sp^2 hybrid orbitals, the three for each atom being used to bond to (*a*) two adjacent carbon atoms, and (*b*) a hydrogen atom. All these bonds will be of the σ type, lying in the same plane. This carbon–hydrogen framework is shown in Figure 19*a*.

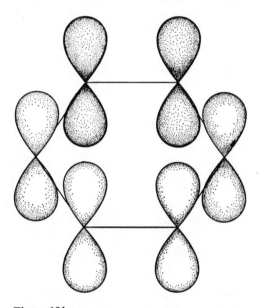

Figure 19*b*

The unused $2p_z$ orbitals of the six carbon atoms in benzene. They lie above and below the plane of the σ bonded framework.

Each carbon atom will also have an unused $2p_z$ orbital, partly filled, and the lobes of these will extend above and below the plane of the σ bonded framework (Figure 19*b*). We can consider two adjacent $2p_z$ lobes to overlap laterally, giving three π bonds, but as it is obvious that any particular $2p_z$ orbital could overlap laterally with the orbital on either side of it, we consider the bonding to result from the overlapping of all the $2p_z$ orbitals taken together.

In other words, we consider the $2p_z$ electrons to be in a molecular orbital made up of the individual $2p_z$ orbitals. The $2p_z$ orbitals are said to be delocalised and the electrons considered to be in a *delocalised molecular orbital*, i.e. the electrons are considered to be spread over all the nuclei and not associated with only two adjacent ones. The molecular orbital is made up of two π molecular orbitals which are delocalised, one above and one below the plane of the σ bonded framework. This is shown in Figure 19c. The concept of a delocalised structure for benzene gives a lower energy than that of conventional Kekulé structures, with three localised π bonds. This structure for benzene also explains the orientating effect of a substituent in the ring; the molecular orbital being 'continuous' above and below the ring, enabling any change in charge due to the substituent to be transmitted to the whole molecule.

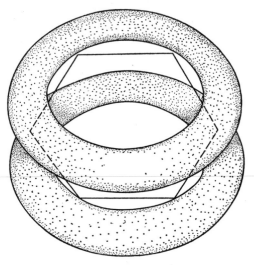

Figure 19c

The $2p_z$ orbitals of benzene considered as a delocalised molecular orbital, consisting of two delocalised π molecular orbitals, above and below the plane of the σ bonded framework.

Finally, we will look at the structures of carbon monoxide and carbon dioxide.

The structure of *carbon monoxide* can be visualised most easily using the molecular orbital approach:

$$\text{Carbon:} \quad 1s^2 2s^2 2p_x^1 2p_y^1$$
$$\text{Oxygen:} \quad 1s^2 2s^2 2p_x^2 2p_y^1 2p_z^1$$

We will distribute the electrons into the available molecular orbitals, combining the atomic orbitals of both atoms. The four $1s$ electrons will enter the $\sigma 1s$ molecular orbital and its corresponding antibonding orbital—

these will effectively cancel out; similarly for the 2s electrons in the σ2s molecular orbitals. We are left with six 2p electrons, and these will enter the σ2p, the $\pi_y 2p$, and the $\pi_z 2p$ molecular orbitals, all of these being bonding orbitals.

Thus the molecule contains three bonds, one being of the σ type, and two being π bonds. It is found from bond length measurements, that the molecule probably contains a carbon–oxygen triple bond, so the molecular

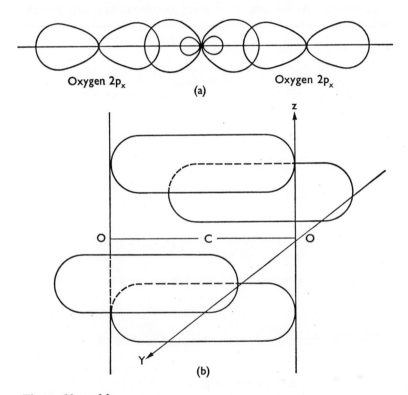

Oxygen 2p$_x$ Oxygen 2p$_x$

(a)

O — C — O

(b)

Figures 20a and b

Carbon dioxide. (a) Overlap of carbon sp hybrid orbitals with oxygen 2p$_x$ orbitals to give σ bonds: O—C—O. (b) The two π molecular orbitals of the molecule formed from unused 2p$_y$ and 2p$_z$ orbitals.

orbital treatment would seem to be satisfactory. It is difficult to postulate a triple bond on valence bond theory, using hybridisation, without using several possible resonance structures.

It is difficult to view the *carbon dioxide* molecule on a molecular orbital approach as, relatively, there are so many electrons to be accommodated. A reasonable picture may be obtained using a valence bond approach.

The structure of oxygen is: $1s^2 2s^2 2p_x^2 2p_y^1 2p_z^1$. However, the $2p$ orbitals are equivalent in energy, and we will write the structure of one oxygen atom as:

$$1s^2 2s^2 2p_x^1 2p_y^2 2p_z^1$$

and:

$$1s^2 2s^2 2p_x^1 2p_y^1 2p_z^2$$

for the other.

If we consider the carbon atom to be sp hybridised from $2s + 2p_x$ orbitals, then we could have a linear O—C—O framework containing σ bonds, by overlap of the two carbon sp hybrid orbitals with the two oxygen $2p_x$ orbitals. This is illustrated in Figure 20a.

However, the oxygen atoms have unused partly filled $2p_y$ and $2p_z$ orbitals between them, and the carbon atom has unused partly filled $2p_y$ and $2p_z$ orbitals. We may therefore visualise side-on overlap between these orbitals to give π bonds. There is therefore a σ bond and a π bond between the carbon atom and each oxygen atom.

It must be admitted that the pictures of CO and CO_2 are something of an oversimplification.

The π bonding is shown in Figure 20b.

Group 5

The elements in this group are generally non-metallic. Nitrogen and phosphorus fall into this category, while there is a changeover from arsenic to antimony, the latter having some metallic properties, forming cations. This is also the case for bismuth. Again the greater ease of ionisation is characteristic of the increased ionic size, going down the group.

All the elements in the group have five electrons in their outer shell, and it would be impossible for them to lose these and become five-valent cations with a rare gas structure.

At the top of the group then, we are dealing strictly with covalency, but in the case of antimony and bismuth, it is possible for three of the outer five electrons (these being p electrons) to be lost to give trivalent cations.

Our concern will be the element nitrogen.

The *nitrogen molecule* is isoelectronic with carbon monoxide, which we considered earlier. It is best considered on molecular orbital theory. The electronic structure of nitrogen is: $1s^2 2s^2 2p_x^1 2p_y^1 2p_z^1$. We are dealing with the combination of two such atoms, and we will feed the electrons into the corresponding available molecular orbitals.

We again find three bonds as the net result, in the form of $\sigma 2p$, $\pi_y 2p$, and $\pi_z 2p$ molecular orbitals. The triple bond is cylindrically and symmetrically disposed about the N—N axis.

The *ammonia molecule* provides some interest. We might think that in this compound, the nitrogen atom would use its three partly filled $2p$ orbitals to overlap with three hydrogen $1s$ orbitals. Because the three p orbitals extend in planes at right angles to each other, we would expect bond angle measurements to give a value of ninety degrees between the nitrogen–hydrogen bonds.

However, this does not turn out to be the case, the measured value being $106° 45'$, which hints at a tetrahedral structure.

If the nitrogen atom uses sp^3 hybrid orbitals, then one of them would be fully occupied, since there are five electrons of principal quantum number 2 available. The three partly filled hybrid orbitals could now overlap with the three hydrogen $1s$ orbitals, and the fully occupied hybrid orbital would constitute the lone pair. The sp^3 hybrid orbitals are tetrahedrally arranged and suggest a value for the H—N—H bond angle of $109°$. The small discrepancy is explained by the repulsion effect of the lone pair, forcing the N—H bonds together.

The ammonium ion NH_4^+ is formed similarly. If the nitrogen atom loses an electron, its electronic structure will become:

$$1s^2 2s^2 2p^2$$

On hybridisation, we would have four partly occupied sp^3 hybrid orbitals. These may then overlap with four hydrogen $1s$ orbitals.

Nitric oxide is also an interesting molecule. We will write the structures for the nitrogen and oxygen atoms thus:

$$\text{Nitrogen:} \quad 1s^2 2s^2 2p_x^1 2p_y^1 2p_z^1$$
$$\text{Oxygen:} \quad 1s^2 2s^2 2p_x^2 2p_y^1 2p_z^1$$

Using a molecular orbital treatment, we may again 'cancel out' the $1s$ and $2s$ electrons into bonding and antibonding orbitals. We have seven $2p$ electrons in atomic orbitals, and they will enter the $\sigma 2p$, $\pi_y 2p$ and $\pi_z 2p$ molecular orbitals with an odd electron in an antibonding $\pi_y^* 2p$ orbital. Thus we may consider the molecule to contain a triple bond of one σ bond and two π bonds, with an unpaired electron in an antibonding orbital which will make it relatively unstable with respect to a nitrogen molecule, the unpaired electron being over the whole molecule (cf. oxygen, page 48).

The valence bond approach to this molecule is unsatisfactory, necessitating several resonance structures.

Group 6

Oxygen and sulphur are the first two elements in the group, and will be our only concern. They are both relatively, highly electronegative, i.e. they are willing to accept electrons. In going from Groups 1 to 5, we have observed a change in properties from the decidedly metallic state of the alkali metals with their ability to form cations and ionic bonds, to elements in Groups 4 and 5 which appear to behave as non-metals and form covalent molecules.

Oxygen and sulphur now mark the return of ionic properties: they both form stable anions, as their electronic configurations are both only two short of their corresponding rare gases in Group 8.

Oxygen has an electronic structure: $1s^2 2s^2 2p_x^2 2p_y^1 2p_z^1$. Now a seemingly satisfactory picture of the oxygen molecule could be obtained by considering the formation of two covalent bonds, by the overlap of the partly filled $2p_y$ and $2p_z$ orbitals respectively, from two oxygen atoms.

However, oxygen exhibits *paramagnetism*, which is similar in kind but far smaller in magnitude to the ferromagnetism exhibited by iron, cobalt and nickel. Paramagnetism is attributed to small magnetic moments produced by the presence of 'unpaired electrons'. In the above representation of the oxygen molecule, there are no unpaired electrons, the two unpaired electrons of one oxygen atom being paired with those of the other.

The molecular orbital approach is able to explain this. Consider two oxygen atoms having the structure written above. Feeding the $1s$ and $2s$ electrons from each atom into the available molecular orbitals, produces fully filled $\sigma 1s$ and $\sigma 2s$ bonding and antibonding orbitals, which effectively cancel one another. We have eight $2p$ electrons altogether. The first six of these will enter the $\sigma 2p$, the $\pi_y 2p$, and the $\pi_z 2p$ bonding molecular orbitals. After these orbitals, come the $\pi_y^* 2p$ and the $\pi_z^* 2p$ antibonding orbitals which are equivalent in energy. We saw in chapter 4, that electrons try to occupy orbitals so that they possess parallel spin as far as is possible. This was certainly the case with atomic orbitals, and there seems no reason why this will not be so for molecular orbitals. Therefore the other two electrons will enter the $\pi_y^* 2p$ and the $\pi_z^* 2p$ antibonding orbitals, one going into each. The molecule contains, as a result, two unpaired electrons. It effectively contains two covalent bonds, as we have six electrons in bonding orbitals effectively, and two in antibonding orbitals, leaving two, two electron bonds, as the net result.

We have seen one possible structure for the *water* molecule on page 33, where we considered the bonding to arise from overlap of 'pure' oxygen $2p$ orbitals with hydrogen $1s$ orbitals.

Instead, let us think of the oxygen atom as using sp^3 hybrid orbitals. Now there are six electrons of principal quantum number 2 eligible for inclusion in the hybrid orbitals. Since there are four hybrid orbitals, two of them will have to be fully filled, and two partly filled. The partly filled ones will overlap successfully with hydrogen $1s$ orbitals, to give two single covalent bonds, and the other two will constitute the 'lone pairs'. The repulsion between the bonding pairs of electrons and the lone pairs forces the bonding pairs towards each other, which accounts for the shrinkage of the HOH bond angle from 109° 31′ to an experimental 104° 30′.

Sulphur has the electronic structure $1s^2 2s^2 2p_x^2 2p_y^2 2p_z^2 3s^2 3p_x^2 3p_y^1 3p_z^1$. Like oxygen, it has two unpaired electrons in p orbitals.

Sulphur exists in several allotropic forms, and it has been found that the basic constituent of them all is a molecule of eight sulphur atoms S_8. The molecule has a ring structure and in it the sulphur atoms are considered to use sp^3 hybridised orbitals (from the $3s$ and $3p$ orbitals). There is overlap between adjacent sulphur atoms by the two partly filled sp^3 hybrid orbitals, and the two fully occupied sp^3 hybrid orbitals constitute lone pairs. These account for the bond angle of 105° 24′ which is less than the tetrahedral angle for sp^3 hybrid orbitals when they are all singly occupied.

Unlike oxygen, sulphur has unfilled d orbitals lying just above its outer electron shell, and these will not be very different in energy. It is possible for the sulphur atom to make use of these in hybridisation, and extend its covalency up to six.

In the molecules of sulphur dioxide and sulphur trioxide, it seems likely that the sulphur atom uses $3d$ orbitals in hybrids to give π bonding with oxygen p orbitals. However the picture of these molecules is uncertain, and resonance pictures are often drawn with alternating double bonds, indicating that there is only partial double bonding present.

The structure of sulphuric acid is also uncertain, but appears also to contain double bonding between the sulphur and oxygen atoms, the π bonding resulting from the use of $3d$ orbitals.

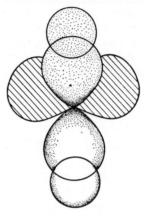

Figure 21

More probable representation of the water molecule. The bonding arises from overlap of oxygen sp^3 hybrid orbitals with hydrogen $1s$ orbitals. The 'lone pairs' on the oxygen are line shaded. The orbitals are displaced tetrahedrally.

Group 7: the halogens

These elements are capable of forming ionic and covalent bonds where the halogen possesses a valency of one. In doing so, they assume the structure of the rare gas adjacent to it, in the next group.

The covalent bonds are formed by overlap of the partly filled outer p orbital of the halogen with a partly filled outer orbital of a second atom. In a chlorine molecule, we will have p–p overlap between two chlorine atoms to give a single σ bond.

Electronegativity increases up the group from astatine to fluorine, with an increase in the ionic nature of the bond formed between the halogen and another element. In other words, towards the top of the group, there will be a tendency for the halogen to pull the shared pair of electrons towards itself and assume a negative charge X—Cl⁻. This is true in such a molecule as hydrogen chloride, and the effect is greatly enhanced by the presence of a polar solvent such as water. The water molecule possesses a distinct charge displacement due to the difference in electronegativity between the oxygen and hydrogen atoms. Thus the 'electron charge cloud' (as the electronic distribution is often referred to) is distorted to favour the oxygen atom. This results in a dipole in the molecule, and the positive end (the hydrogens) will attract the negative ends of other water molecules—we say water is *hydrogen-*

bonded. This however is not the only effect, for the dipole in the water molecule may attract that of the hydrogen chloride. The negative (oxygen) end of the water molecule can attract the hydrogen (positive) end of a hydrogen chloride molecule. This will result in a breakage of the H—Cl bond with the liberation of the Cl^- ion and the formation of the hydroxonium ion H_3O^+. Thus water has enabled a covalently bonded hydrogen chloride molecule to behave as an electrolyte.

We have mentioned that water exhibits hydrogen bonding. We meet another molecule that displays this property in the halogen group: hydrogen fluoride. Like the oxygen atom, fluorine is highly electronegative relative to a hydrogen atom. Now we may consider the bonding in the HF molecule to result from an overlap between a partly filled hydrogen $1s$ orbital and the partly filled $2p_z$ orbital of the fluorine atom. However the difference in electronegativity between the two atoms will result in the charge cloud being shifted towards the fluorine atom. A dipole will be produced F^-—H^+, and two such dipoles may attract electrostatically thus:

$$F^-—H^+\ldots F^-—H^+\ldots F^-—H^+\ldots$$

Hydrogen bonding thus produces a form of polymerisation—the unit of molecules formed, having a higher molecular weight than that expected from the consideration of the compound as a single molecule. Thus water and hydrogen fluoride have far higher boiling points than would be expected from their low molecular weights of eighteen and twenty respectively.

Many interhalogen compounds are known of the type XY_3, XY_5 and XY_7, where X and Y are different halogens, and the electronegativity of X is less than that of Y.

In such compounds as ClF_3, the chlorine atom appears to use sp^3d hybrid orbitals, two of the orbitals containing lone pairs of electrons, the other three, being partly filled, will be used for bonding with three fluorine partly filled p orbitals (one from each atom).

The transition elements

In the middle of the Periodic Table we have the transition elements—these are elements which possess an incompletely filled inner d orbital. Thus the first series of transition elements ranges from scandium to zinc. Scandium has the electronic structure: $1s^2 2s^2 2p^6 3s^2 3p^6 3d^1 4s^2$, and the elements which follow are characterised by the filling up of the $3d$ orbital to zinc with a structure: $1s^2 2s^2 2p^6 3s^2 3p^6 3d^{10} 4s^2$. As can be seen from the structure of zinc, it is not strictly a transition element, but the $4p$ orbitals are not far away in terms of energy and it could use these in complex formation which will be mentioned later.

A similar series of elements occurs from the element yttrium with a structure $(Zn) 4p^6 4d^1 5s^2$ to cadmium $(Zn) 4p^6 4d^{10} 5s^2$. These elements will be characterised by the filling up of the $4d$ orbital. Again cadmium is not a transition metal on this basis.

Finally, the series of elements from hafnium to mercury constitute the third series of transition elements, and these are characterised by the filling up of the $5d$ orbital. Mercury has a completely filled $5d$ orbital and is not a transition metal, although it also forms complexes.

The presence of an incompletely filled d orbital lying close (in terms of energy) to available s and p orbitals accounts for the considerable hybridisation, variable valency and complex compound formation, characteristic of transition elements.

A *complex compound* is one in which an atom has attached to it more atoms than would be thought possible from its normal valency. These extra atoms provide all the electrons needed to make the extra bonds, the qualification being that the particular atom being 'complexed' has vacant orbitals which are low-lying in terms of energy. The atoms which become attached in this manner are often termed *ligands*, and the number of attached ligands is known as the *coordination number*.

Our main consideration will be the First Series of transition elements from scandium to zinc. Scandium and zinc are not true transition elements as they each exhibit only one valency state in each case (three and two respectively), and although scandium has an incompletely filled inner d orbital and by definition is a transition element, it does not behave like one. Beside exhibiting only one valency, it forms no complex compounds.

Variable valency

We have mentioned that the transition elements show variable valency— the variation can be quite considerable. Thus vanadium may have valence states of 5, 4, 3, 2, while manganese may have states of 7, 6, 4, 3, 2. It should be emphasised that here we are talking about valency and not coordination number, thus while copper shows only valency states of one and two (three under right conditions), it may exhibit coordination numbers in the bivalent ion state Cu^{2+} of 4 and 6, while in the univalent ion state Cu^+, it may exhibit coordination of two and four.

Copper has the electronic structure: $1s^2 2s^2 2p^6 3s^2 3p^6 3d^{10} 4s^1$—it may lose one electron from the outer s orbital and become a Cu^+ ion. Loss of two electrons will leave a copper (II) ion Cu^{2+}—with an outer structure $3d^9$. This copper (II) ion has a structure similar to other transition metal ions with a characteristic incompletely filled d orbital. Thus, besides combining ionically with bivalent anions, it may form complex compounds.

As well as forming ions, copper may form covalent bonds in the bivalent state, such as copper (II) oxide and copper (II) chloride. These in general are less stable than the univalent covalent compounds of copper, and generally decompose on heat into the latter.

The copper (I) ion Cu^+ is present in copper (I) sulphate Cu_2SO_4 but other copper (I) compounds appear to be covalent, though the Cu^+ ion is stabilised by complex ion formation.

The various valency states of the other transition metals are numerous and are at a maximum in manganese. Those elements before manganese are able to use their $3d$ and $4s$ electrons in ionic and covalent bonding, so that manganese may have a maximum valency of seven, while that of titanium is four.

After manganese, the most frequently encountered valency state is two, with three and one to a lesser extent.

Complex compounds

We will mention a few of these, classed by coordination number, as the bonding provides some interest from the point of view of hybridisation.

Coordination number two

This is fulfilled in complexes of the silver Ag^+ and gold Au^+ ions, in the complexes $[Ag(NH_3)_2]^+$ and $[Au(CN)_2]^-$ (these being in the second and third series respectively).

Silver has the electronic structure $(Kr)\ 4s^2 4p^6 4d^{10} 5s^1$. Loss of an electron leads to a completely filled d orbital, and as would be expected, this is the most stable valency state for the metal. However, the $5s$ and the $5p$ orbitals are close in energy to the $4d$ orbitals, and they will be available to co-ordinating ligands.

Thus:

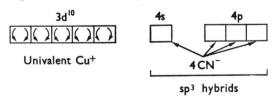

The vacant s and p_x orbitals may be hybridised (we could take the p_y or the p_z) to give two sp hybrid orbitals. The bonding is *linear*, and will result as the two ammonia molecules donate their lone pairs of electrons into the vacant hybrid orbitals.

Coordination number four

Complexes of coordination number three are rare but there are many of coordination number four. They are mostly *tetrahedral* and will contain sp^3 hybridised orbitals, which are characteristically disposed in this way. An example of a tetrahedral complex is the cyano complex of the copper (I) ion $[Cu(CN)_4]^{3-}$.

Considering the outer orbitals only of the Cu^+ ion:

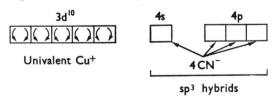

Four tetrahedral bonds are formed by donation of the electrons from four cyanide ions into the sp^3 hybrid orbitals.

However a second type of complex is encountered for this coordination number. It is characterised by dsp^2 hybridised orbitals. This is the case in the tetramminecopper (II) ion $[Cu(NH_3)_4]^{2+}$.

Considering the copper (II) ion:

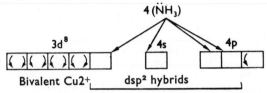

The unusual arrangement in the copper (II) ion of four fully filled and one empty d orbitals is due to a splitting of the energy levels of the d orbitals. Up to now, we have always considered the five of them to be equivalent in energy, but it seems that the approach of the ammonia molecule ligands is able to separate one of the d orbitals to a position of higher energy—the other four are occupied in preference as a result. The result is the formation of dsp^2 hybrid orbitals using the vacant $4s$ and $4p$ orbitals again. This time the molecule is square planar in structure, this being characteristic of dsp^2 hybridisation.

The splitting effect of incoming ligands is obtained from a treatment known as *ligand field theory*, which we will not consider in any more detail than this.

Coordination number six

Compounds of coordination number five are comparatively rare. The complexes of coordination number six are mostly *octahedral*, and contain d^2sp^3 hybrid bonds.

Such an example is the hexacyanoferrate complex $[Fe(CN)_6]^{3-}$.

The ferric ion has an electronic structure $1s^2 2s^2 2p^6 3s^2 3p^6 3d^5$, but again, the incoming cyanide ligands change the expected arrangement of five partly filled d orbitals. This time there is a splitting to two energy levels—the lower one accounting for *three* of the d orbitals, the other *two* being at a higher energy level. As a result, the iron (III) ion electrons tend to occupy only three of the $3d$ orbitals, leaving the other two empty to take part in d^2sp^3 hybridisation. Thus:

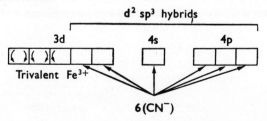

However with a ligand which is not capable of producing such a pronounced splitting, such as the ammonia molecule, we obtain a complex with five unpaired electrons, i.e. with the expected iron (III) ion configuration retained.

Thus:

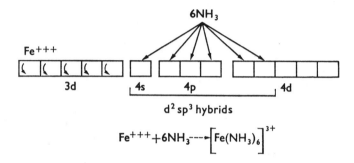

$$Fe^{+++} + 6NH_3 \dashrightarrow \left[Fe(NH_3)_6 \right]^{3+}$$

The structure of the molecule is again that of the geometry of d^2sp^3 hybrid orbitals, but there is a huge difference in the paramagnetism exhibited by the molecule. Thus, in the hexacyanoferrate complex, there is only one unpaired electron—with a low resultant magnetic moment. The ammonia complex of the iron (III) ion has five unpaired electrons, with a high magnetic moment, and this distinction has been a major contribution in ascertaining the structure of the different ions.

In this final chapter, we have studied a variety of molecules made up of some of the more familiar elements, in an attempt to demonstrate the application of the ideas presented in the previous chapters.

As can be seen, quite a few concepts have had to be introduced to secure even a reasonable collaboration with physical observation. None the less, the orbital approach does tell us something about the geometry of molecules, and it is fortunate that modern methods of determining such quantities as bond lengths and bond angles are able to guide its application. Although modern valency seems to become increasingly mathematical, it is important to realise that a molecular structure does not tumble out as the last line of a calculation. There must always be reference to what we know from observing the behaviour of the molecule.

We have come a long way from the relatively simple theory of Bohr—its inadequacies were no doubt apparent at the time and they are even more so now, but this will no doubt be true of the complex picture we have at the moment.

Book list

ADDISON, W. E. *Structural Principles of Inorganic Compounds*. Longman, 1963.

BROGLIE, L. DE. *New Perspectives in Physics*. Oliver & Boyd, 1960.

BROWN, G. I. *A New Guide to Modern Valency Theory*. Longman, 1967.

CARTMELL, E. and FOWLES, G. W. A. *Valency and Molecular Structure*, 2nd edn. Butterworths, 1961.

COULSON, C. A. *Valence*, 2nd edn. O.U.P., 1961.

GRAY, H. B. *Electrons and Chemical Bonding*. New York, Benjamin, 1964.

HERZBERG, G. *Atomic Spectra and Atomic Structure*, new edn. Dover Publications, 1944.

HESLOP, R. B. and ROBINSON, P. L. *Inorganic Chemistry*, 2nd edn. Elsevier, 1962.

LINNETT, W. J. *Wave Mechanics and Valency*, new edn. Methuen, 1960.

PAULING, L. and HAYWARD, R. *The Architecture of Molecules*. Freeman, 1965.

PIMENTEL, G. C. *Chemical Education Material Study: Chemistry—An Experimental Science*. Text and Teacher's Manual. New York, Freeman, 1963.

SANDERSON, R. T. *Chemical Periodicity*. Reinhold: Chapman & Hall, 1960.

SPICE, E. J. *Chemical Binding and Structure*. Pergamon, 1964.

WILD, K. and NELLIST, J. *Structure and Behaviour*. Longman, 1970.

Index